This report, No. 17-M-01, can be ordered from the National Assessment of Educational Progress at Educational Testing Service, Rosedale Road, Princeton, New Jersey 08541-0001.

Library of Congress, Catalog Card Number: 88-61010

ISBN 0-88685-072-X

The work upon which this publication is based was performed pursuant to Grant No. NIE-G-83-0011 of the Office for Educational Research and Improvement. It does not, however, necessarily reflect the views of that agency.

Educational Testing Service is an equal opportunity/affirmative action employer.

Educational Testing Service, ETS, and ⓔⓣⓢ® are registered trademarks of Educational Testing Service.

THE NATION'S REPORT CARD

The Mathematics Report Card
Are We Measuring Up?

Trends and Achievement Based on the 1986 National Assessment

John A. Dossey □ Ina V. S. Mullis □ Mary M. Lindquist □ Donald L. Chambers

EDUCATIONAL TESTING SERVICE

June 1988

Report No: 17-M-01

CONTENTS

ABOUT THIS REPORT

T HE MATHEMATICS *Report Card*, spanning nearly a decade-and-a-half and four national surveys, is the most comprehensive profile ever of the mathematical skills and knowledge of young Americans. This extensive report merits particularly close attention from educators and policy leaders, whose decisions can improve the state of mathematics education in the United States.

As a society on the threshold of the 21st century, are we measuring up? These results say no. Findings from the 1986 mathematics assessment parallel those from recent assessments in reading, writing, and literacy, in which the Nation's Report Card has documented a critical shortage of effective reasoning skills among our young people. Although more students appear to have mastered basic mathematical skills and concepts in recent years, few achieve the higher range of mathematics proficiency. Our nation must address this deficit if it is to thrive in the technological era facing us.

The time for reform also is upon us. Every year, nearly 1.5 million American 17-year-olds near the end of high school without much-needed mathematical reasoning skills. Fully a third of our 13-year-olds haven't mastered skills universally taught in elementary school. Few youngsters can put mathematics to work effectively in solving everyday problems, and such practical activity is absent from most classrooms.

But America's education system has risen to challenges before, providing basic education to more of its population than any other country in the world. At this critical point, I urge you to consider NAEP's mathematics findings in light of the human potential at stake and the economic demands before us.

Gregory R. Anrig
President
Educational Testing Service

7

OVERVIEW

Why Mathematics Counts

THE SKILLS and expertise of a country's workforce are the foundation of its economic success. Lately, in our country, this foundation appears too fragile to withstand the challenges of the 21st century.

■ The most recent international mathematics study reported that average Japanese students exhibited higher levels of achievement than the top 5 percent of American students enrolled in college preparatory mathematics courses.[1] As a case in point, a Japanese semiconductor company recently opening a plant in the Southeastern United States had to use college students at the graduate level to perform statistical quality control functions; the same jobs were performed by high-school graduates in Japan.[2]

■ One out of three major corporations already provides new workers with basic reading, writing, and arithmetic courses. If current demographic and economic trends continue, American businesses will hire a million new people a year who can't read, write, or count. Teaching them how, and absorbing the lost productivity while they are learning, will cost industry $25 billion a year for as long as it takes—and nobody seems to know how long that will be.[3]

> . . . average Japanese students exhibited higher levels of achievement than the top 5 percent of American students enrolled in college preparatory mathematics courses.

---

[1] Curtis McKnight, et al., *The Underachieving Curriculum: Assessing U.S. School Mathematics from an International Perspective*. A National Report on the Second International Mathematics Study, International Association for the Evaluation of Education Achievement, Stipes Publishing Company, Champaign, IL, 1987.

[2] George Gilder, "Chip Sense and Nonsense," *Wall Street Journal*, April 2, 1987.

[3] David Kearns, Chairman and Chief Executive Officer, Xerox Corporation, *Learning to Be Literate in America*, Foreword, 1987.

■ American colleges have reported a 10- to 30-percent rise in demand over the past several years for remedial coursework in mathematics for incoming freshmen. As diagnosed in one study, these young people are not defined as at-risk, yet they are not workforce ready. For the at-risk populations, the mismatch between workplace needs and workforce skills is even greater.[4]

■ Looking toward the year 2000, the fastest-growing occupations require employees to have much higher math, language, and reasoning capabilities than do current occupations.[5]

Too many students leave high school without the mathematical understanding that will allow them to participate fully as workers and citizens in contemporary society. As these young people enter universities and businesses, American college faculty and employers must anticipate additional burdens. As long as the supply of adequately prepared precollegiate students remains substandard, it will be difficult for these institutions to assume the dual responsibility of remedial and specialized training; and without highly trained personnel, the United States risks forfeiting its competitive edge in world and domestic markets.

Even for those working in less scientifically specialized areas, technological innovations require the ability to learn and adapt to new conditions. Studies of technological change have reached differing conclusions as to the nature and extent of its impact on job skill requirements, but it is certain that the current generation of students will need to work with increasingly large and complex bodies of information in performing even basic tasks. From the basic computational skills required to organize and track large-scale shipments of merchandise to the higher-level expertise necessary to make technological discoveries, it is clear that mathematical abilities will be critical to our nation's continued economic success.

Highlights from NAEP's Mathematics Assessments

NAEP's 1986 mathematics assessment provides a timely account of student achievement in this vital subject, and the results highlight the need for even greater commitment to school mathematics programs. Trends across four assessments since 1973 offer a comprehensive view of achievement patterns for students at ages 9, 13, and 17.

■ Recent national trends in mathematics performance are somewhat encouraging, particularly for students at ages 9 and 17. Subpopulations

---

[4] *The Fourth R: Workforce Readiness*. National Alliance of Business, November 1987, p. 5.

[5] *Workforce 2000: Work and Workers for the 21st Century*. Hudson Institute, Indianapolis, IN, June 1987.

of students who performed comparatively poorly in past assessments have shown significant improvement in average proficiency since 1978: at all three ages, Black and Hispanic students made appreciable gains, as did students living in the Southeast.

■ While average performance has improved since 1978, the gains have been confined primarily to lower-order skills. The highest level of performance attained by any substantial proportion of students in 1986 reflects only moderately complex skills and understandings. Most students, even at age 17, do not possess the breadth and depth of mathematics proficiency needed for advanced study in secondary school mathematics.

While we may be recovering from the doldrums of poor performance that characterized the 1970s, it is crucial that we do even better to reach expected or hoped-for levels of achievement. Improvements are needed, not only in average proficiency, but also in the number of students who reach the upper levels of performance.

Other Findings

■ Discrepancies between the level of mathematics commonly taught in elementary, middle, and high schools and what students know and can do in the subject appear to increase over the school years, especially for Black and Hispanic students. Only about half of all the 17-year-olds in the 1986 assessment reached a level of proficiency associated with material taught in junior high school mathematics.

■ Mathematics instruction in 1986, as in previous years, continues to be dominated by teacher explanations, chalkboard presentations, and reliance on textbooks and workbooks. More innovative forms of instruction—such as those involving small group activities, laboratory work, and special projects—remain disappointingly rare.

■ Students reported more homework and testing in mathematics in 1986 than in previous assessments, perhaps indicating a growth in academic expectations in schools.

■ Students appear to gain basic mathematical knowledge and skills in numbers and operations between grades 3 and 7, while higher-level applications in numbers and operations develop steadily across the three grade levels. Females outperformed males in the area of basic knowledge and skills, while males had the advantage in higher-level applications.

■ Although the role of technology in the mathematics classroom appears to be changing, the benefits of using computers and calculators seem to be available primarily to small proportions of students who are in the upper range of ability or in the upper grades.

■ Although more high school students in 1986 than in previous years reported taking higher-level mathematics courses, including Algebra II, Geometry, and Calculus, the overall percentage of students taking these advanced courses remains disappointingly low.

■ High school students whose parents encourage mathematics course-taking and have higher levels of education tend to exhibit higher mathematics proficiency than those who lack this home support.

■ Students who enjoy mathematics and perceive its relevance to everyday life tend to have higher proficiency scores than students with more negative perspectives. At the same time, students' enjoyment of and confidence in mathematics appear to wane as they progress through their schooling. Most perceive that the subject is composed mainly of rule memorization, and expect to have little use for mathematical skills in their future work lives.

This report chronicles trends in proficiency across four mathematics assessments conducted in 1972-73, 1977-78, 1981-82, and 1985-86.

Summary of Assessment Procedures

This report chronicles trends in proficiency across four mathematics assessments conducted in 1972-73, 1977-78, 1981-82, and 1985-86. (For convenience, each assessment will be referred to by the last half of the school year in which it occurred—1973, 1978, 1982, and 1986.) Each of the four mathematics assessments involved nationally representative samples of 9-, 13-, and 17-year-olds, and together the assessments generated data from a total of 150,000 students for the examination of trends. In the 1986 assessment, NAEP sampled students by grade as well as age, making available a second data set based on 34,000 additional students in grades 3, 7, and 11.

The mathematics assessments included both open-ended and multiple-choice questions covering a wide range of content and process areas. Student background information gathered during each administration permits consideration of trends in relation to school, home, and attitudinal factors.

The data were analyzed using Item Response Theory (IRT) scaling technology and are summarized on a common scale (0 to 500) to facilitate direct comparisons across assessment years for age groups and subpopulations. To provide a basis for interpreting the results, the report describes what stu-

11

dents attaining different proficiency levels on the scale are able to do. Based on the assessment results, five levels of proficiency have been defined:

Level 150   Simple Arithmetic Facts

Level 200   Beginning Skills and Understanding

Level 250   Basic Operations and Beginning Problem Solving

Level 300   Moderately Complex Procedures and Reasoning

Level 350   Multi-step Problem Solving and Algebra

NAEP's mathematics scale was computed as a weighted composite of proficiency on five content area subscales—knowledge and skills, higher-level applications, measurement, geometry, and algebra. Thus, for the most recent assessment, results are also available indicating students' relative strengths and weaknesses across these content areas.

Reflections

The assessment findings show both encouraging and discouraging trends for mathematics education in the United States. It is encouraging to see improvements in performance occurring across such a wide segment of the student population, especially among Black and Hispanic students and those in the Southeast. However, this good news must be tempered by continuing concern over the generally low levels of performance exhibited by most high school students and by the fact that the majority of improvement shown resulted from increased performance in low-level skills.

Evidence concerning the nature of mathematics education suggests that the curriculum continues to be dominated by paper-and-pencil drills on basic computation. Little evidence appears of any widespread use of calculators, computers, or mathematics projects. This picture reflects classrooms more concerned with students' rote use of procedures than with their understanding of concepts and development of higher-order thinking skills. The continuance of such a pattern offers little hope that the mathematics education of our children will achieve the goals being set by the recent educational excellence movement.

Findings from the 1986 assessment, however, indicate that recent reforms directed toward increasing requirements in high school mathematics education, and schooling in general, may be beginning to have some effect in raising the overall performance of our students.

> It is encouraging to see improvements in performance occurring across such a wide segment of the student population . . .

> Little evidence appears of any widespread use of calculators, computers, or mathematics projects.

12

Achieving a higher-quality mathematics curriculum across schools in the United States will require new materials, effective instructional methods, and improved means of evaluating student performance. There are many well-qualified and dedicated teachers in our classrooms capable of promoting improved ways of learning.[6] In order to do so, our teachers will need the support of administrators, parents, and the public at large. No longer can society afford to view mathematics as a subject for a chosen few or as a domain solely composed of arithmetic skills. Students must come to see it as a way of thinking, communicating, and resolving problems. Until American schools move toward these more ambitious goals in mathematics instruction, there is little hope that current levels of achievement will show any appreciable gain.

---

[6]*And Gladly Teach: A Ford Foundation Report on the Urban Mathematics Collaborative*. New York: The Ford Foundation, 1987.

Part I
Improvement or Impasse?

Trends in Mathematics Proficiency and Relative Strengths and Weaknesses

Introduction

AFTER A wave of reports, widely recounted in the national press, we are quite used to being told about the sad state of mathematics education in our country. *Educating Americans for the 21st Century* reported that alarming numbers of students are ill-equipped to work in and contribute to our technological society because of inadequate grounding in mathematics and science.[1] The Second International Mathematics Study (SIMS) found that the U.S. standing is very low relative to other countries, both in terms of the proportion of high school students enrolled in advanced mathematics courses and how much mathematics those students know. The achievement of our precalculus students (the majority of twelfth-grade college-preparatory mathematics students) was substantially below average, in some cases ranking lowest among the advanced industrialized countries.[2] Our nation competes in technologically

. . . the U.S. standing is very low relative to other countries . . .

---

[1] *Educating Americans for the 21st Century: A Plan of Action for Improving Mathematics, Science and Technology Education for All American Elementary and Secondary Students So That Their Achievement Is the Best in the World by 1995*. A Report to the American People and the National Science Board, the National Science Board Commission on Precollege Education in Mathematics, Science, and Technology, 1983.

[2] Curtis McKnight, et al., *The Underachieving Curriculum: Assessing U.S. School Mathematics from an International Perspective*. A National Report on the Second International Mathematics Study, International Association for the Evaluation of Education Achievement, Stipes Publishing Company, Champaign, IL 1987.

sophisticated economic markets; yet, from an international perspective, our precollege pipeline is supplying relatively low numbers of high-school graduates prepared to engage in the specialized study necessary for careers in technical fields.

During the last decade, attempts to improve mathematics education have been made in response to demands for reform. State legislatures have increased high-school graduation requirements and mandated competency tests for teachers as well as students. Publishers are including more challenging materials in their kits and texts, research projects and model curricula are springing up, and the National Council of Teachers of Mathematics (NCTM) has issued a draft of new curriculum standards.[3]

Publishers are including more challenging materials in their kits and texts . . .

Some signs of progress toward improving mathematics education are evident in the results of the 1986 NAEP mathematics assessment. Trends from previous assessments of 9-, 13-, and 17-year-olds indicate recent improvements in the mathematics proficiency of American school children at all three age levels. Particularly encouraging is that Black and Hispanic students as well as students living in the Southeast continued to make progress in narrowing their substantial gap in performance compared to other groups of students.

However, the positive outlook suggested by these findings must be tempered by the realization that the gains primarily resulted from improved performance in lower-level skills and basic concepts—material generally thought to be learned in elementary or perhaps middle schools. While the effects of instructional emphasis on basic computational skills in the lower grades are clear in the NAEP data and seem to be producing dividends, students simultaneously need to broaden their repertoire of problem-solving strategies and extend their understanding of arithmetic operations into other content areas (e.g., geometry and algebra). A pattern of improvement concentrated in the area of basic skills implies severe consequences for our nation's continued creative technological leadership in the global marketplace.

. . . the effects of instructional emphasis on basic computational skills in the lower grades are clear in the NAEP data and seem to be producing dividends . . .

Further, despite signs of their progress across time, the 1986 performance of 17-year-old students was dismal. The discrepancy between generally accepted curricula at various grade levels vis-á-vis what students actually know and can do appears to widen as students progress through school. By age 17, only half the high-school students demonstrated an understanding of even moderately complex mathematical procedures (material generally thought to be introduced in junior high schools) and hardly any (6 percent) could solve multi-step problems, especially if they involved understanding algebra or geometry. Considering the large proportion of older students who

By age 17, only half the high-school students demonstrated an understanding of even moderately complex mathematical procedures . . .

---

[3]*Curriculum and Evaluation Standards for School Mathematics*. National Council of Teachers of Mathematics, Inc., Working Draft, October 1987.

have dropped out of school, and the comparatively poor performance of students in some demographic subpopulations, this information is particularly sobering.

A nation's mathematical expertise represents a critical filter for the future success of its economic, technological, and scientific growth. Continued efforts toward improving the design, delivery, and evaluation of high-quality mathematics programs are necessary if American schools are to build on the strengths identified in the 1986 assessment and increase the U.S. mathematics yield to an internationally competitive level.

Part I of this report discusses trends in proficiency across the 13-year period from 1973 to 1986 and describes what students know and can do in mathematics. Chapter 1 presents changes in average proficiency across four assessments of mathematics for the nation and demographic subpopulations. Chapter 2 describes the mathematical competencies attained by students at five performance levels and discusses trends in the percentages of students reaching each level. Chapter 3 presents information about the relative strengths and weaknesses of students across five mathematics content areas—knowledge and skills in numbers and operations, higher-level applications in numbers and operations, measurement, geometry, and algebra.

The chapters in Part II include information about key variables associated with student learning in mathematics, including classroom instruction, teaching materials, student perceptions of the discipline, teacher and parental expectations, and course enrollment.

A Note About Interpretations

Interpreting the assessment results—attempting to put them into a "real world" context, advancing plausible explanations of effects, and suggesting possible courses of action—will always be an art, not a science. No one can control all the possible variables affecting a survey. Also, any particular change in achievement may be explained in many ways or perhaps not at all. The interpretative remarks in this report represent the professional judgments of NAEP staff and consultants and must stand the tests of reason and the reader's knowledge and experience. However, these conjectures represent one way of stimulating the debate necessary to achieve a full understanding of the findings and implement appropriate action.

CHAPTER 1
Signs of Progress?

Trends in Overall Mathematics Performance for the Nation and Demographic Subgroups

National Trends: 1973-1986

THE NATIONAL Assessment of Educational Progress (NAEP) has summarized trends in average mathematics proficiency for 9-, 13-, and 17-year-olds on a common scale ranging from 0 to 500.[1] NAEP also has characterized student performance at five levels on the scale: Level 150—Simple Arithmetic Facts, Level 200—Beginning Skills and Understanding, Level 250—Basic Operations and Beginning Problem Solving, Level 300—Moderately Complex Procedures and Reasoning, and Level 350—Multi-step Problem Solving and Algebra. This chapter presents trends in average mathematics proficiency for students at ages 9, 13, and 17, while Chapter 2 presents trends in performance at each of the five levels on the scale.

FIGURE 1.1 provides an overall index of national trends in mathematics proficiency for 9-, 13-, and 17-year-olds during the 13-year period from 1973 to 1986. The results for the 1978, 1982, and 1986 assessments are based on a newly-conducted trend analysis of the data collected in those assessments,

---

[1]Computed as a weighted composite of student performance on five content area subscales (i.e., Knowledge and Skills/Numbers and Operations, Higher-level Applications/Numbers and Operations, Measurement, Geometry, and Relations and Functions), the NAEP mathematics scale takes the form of a hypothetical 500-item test composed of questions reflecting the proportional weighting of the subscales.

National Trends in Average
Mathematics Proficiency for
9-, 13-, and 17-Year-Olds: 1973-1986

FIGURE 1.1

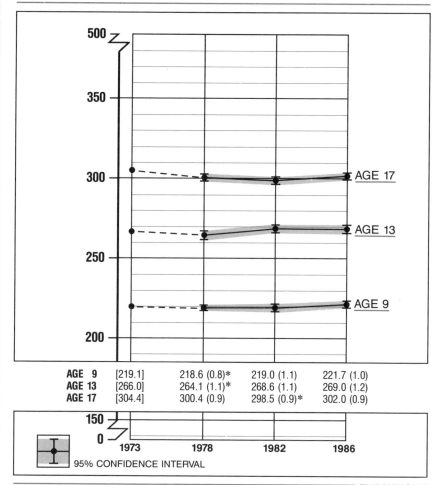

AGE 9	[219.1]	218.6 (0.8)*	219.0 (1.1)	221.7 (1.0)
AGE 13	[266.0]	264.1 (1.1)*	268.6 (1.1)	269.0 (1.2)
AGE 17	[304.4]	300.4 (0.9)	298.5 (0.9)*	302.0 (0.9)

[- - -] Extrapolated from previous NAEP analyses.
* Statistically significant difference from 1986 at the .05 level.
Jackknifed standard errors are presented in parentheses.

THE NATION'S
REPORT
CARD

while the results for 1973 (dotted line) are extrapolated from previous NAEP analyses.[2] (Please refer to the Procedural Appendix for details about the scaling and extrapolation methodology.)

Nine-year-olds—As a result of recent improvements, 9-year-olds showed significant gains in mathematics proficiency during the eight-year period

[2] *The Third National Mathematics Assessment: Results, Trends, and Issues.* National Assessment of Educational Progress, Education Commission of the States, 1983. (See Procedural Appendix for a comparison of results using previous analytical methods.)

from 1978 to 1986. In the 13-year span covered by NAEP's four mathematics assessments, their performance was quite stable across the 1970s, but improved between 1982 and 1986.

Thirteen-year-olds — Thirteen-year-olds also showed significant improvement during the eight-year period from 1978 to 1986, but the pattern differed from that shown by 9-year-olds. After a slight decline between 1973 and 1978, student performance improved between 1978 and 1982, and then leveled off in 1986.

Seventeen-year-olds — The mathematics performance of 17-year-olds declined from 1973 to 1978 and the negative trend continued, although abated, into the early 1980s. However, the most recent assessment showed a significant upturn between 1982 and 1986.

Although not particularly eye-catching or dramatic, the national trends indicate recent improvements for all three age groups. For the two younger age groups, the significant increases between 1978 and 1986 indicate that performance is gradually improving, albeit somewhat unevenly. At age 17, however, the question remains whether the recent upturn in performance represents the beginning of a positive trend back to and even beyond previous achievement levels or only an abatement of previous declines.

For at least the last 15 years, there has been continuing concern about national declines in student test scores, particularly at the high-school level. However, recent results from a number of data bases, including the NAEP trends in reading and writing as well as the modest upturn in SAT scores, indicate that our country seems to be recovering from these losses. Thus, it is especially heartening that NAEP's trends in mathematics proficiency seem to reinforce the positive trends found in other large-scale studies.[3]

In addition to examining the agreement between NAEP trends in mathematics proficiency and other achievement indicators, the assessment design permits looking at patterns for birth-year cohorts of students. Changes for

> For at least the last 15 years, there has been continuing concern about national declines in student test scores . . .

---

[3] *National Report, College Bound Seniors, 1987 Profile of SAT and Achievement Test Takers*. The College Board, 1987.

Educational Achievement: Explanations and Implications of Recent Trends. Congress of the United States, Congressional Budget Office, 1987.

Arthur Applebee, Judith Langer, and Ina Mullis, *Writing Trends Across the Decade, 1974-84*. National Assessment of Educational Progress, Educational Testing Service, 1986.

William Turnbull, *Student Change, Program Change: Why SAT Scores Kept Falling*. College Board Report, No. 85-2, 1985.

The Reading Report Card, Progress Toward Excellence in Our Schools, Trends in Reading over Four National Assessments, 1971-1984. National Assessment of Educational Progress. Educational Testing Service, 1985.

Donald Rock, et. al., *Excellence in High School Education: Cross-Sectional Study, 1972-1980, Final Report*. Educational Testing Service, 1984.

students born in the same year can be identified and compared as these students move through school. For older students, the performance of their birth-year cohorts in previous assessments may help explain current trends.[4]

For example, the NAEP mathematics results indicate that students born in 1965 declined in performance at both ages 13 and 17 compared to students born earlier. Further, those students born four years later in 1969 showed improvements at both ages 13 and 17 compared to the students born in 1965. Thus, it appears that both the recent declines and improvements at age 17 may reflect declines and improvements made by this group of students when they were 13. Although the same cohort pattern is not reflected in the results for 9-year-olds, the relationships at ages 13 and 17 suggest that the causes underlying the recent improvements at age 17 extend beyond changes currently being made to strengthen high-school graduation requirements.

Trends for Demographic Subpopulations

In several instances, trends for particular subpopulations of students vary significantly from the national trends. Generally, between 1978 and 1986 these variations have had the effect of narrowing differences in performance between traditionally advantaged and disadvantaged groups. For example, Black students and to some extent Hispanic students have closed the performance gaps relative to their White peers, although the differences still remain substantial. Similarly, the southeastern region showed comparatively larger and more consistent gains than the other three regions of the country. Students in the Southeast improved significantly during the eight-year period from 1978 to 1986 at all three age levels.

Trends in Proficiency by Race/Ethnicity

FIGURE 1.2 displays trends in average mathematics proficiency for White, Black, and Hispanic students. At ages 9 and 13, Black students have shown steady improvement across the 13-year period from 1973 to 1986, improving significantly from 1978 to 1982 and again from 1982 to 1986. At age 17, however, Black students showed relatively consistent performance between 1973 and 1978, before improving significantly between 1978 and 1986.

At age 9, trends for Hispanic students indicate a pattern of very slight, gradual improvement with each successive assessment. At the older ages,

At the older ages, Hispanic students showed recent improvements.

---

[4] *Educational Achievement: Explanations and Implications of Recent Trends.* Congress of the United States, Congressional Budget Office, 1987.

The Reading Report Card, Progress Toward Excellence in Our Schools, Trends in Reading over Four National Assessments, 1971-1984. National Assessment of Educational Progress, Educational Testing Service, 1985.

Trends in Average Mathematics Proficiency for 9-, 13-, and 17-Year-Olds by Race/Ethnicity: 1973-1986

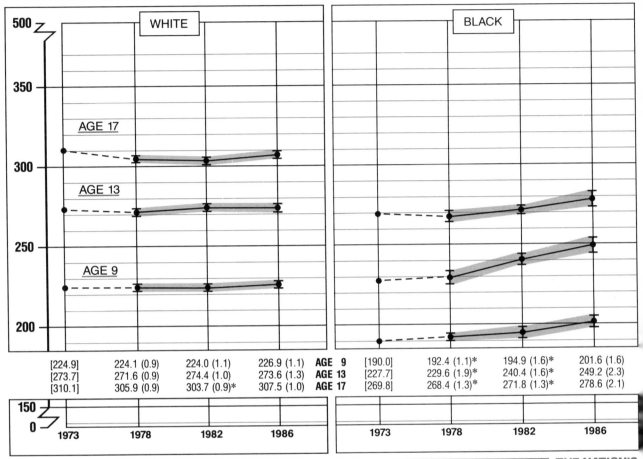

[224.9]	224.1 (0.9)	224.0 (1.1)	226.9 (1.1)	**AGE 9**	[190.0]	192.4 (1.1)*	194.9 (1.6)*	201.6 (1.6)
[273.7]	271.6 (0.9)	274.4 (1.0)	273.6 (1.3)	**AGE 13**	[227.7]	229.6 (1.9)*	240.4 (1.6)*	249.2 (2.3)
[310.1]	305.9 (0.9)	303.7 (0.9)*	307.5 (1.0)	**AGE 17**	[269.8]	268.4 (1.3)*	271.8 (1.3)*	278.6 (2.1)

[– – –] Extrapolated from previous NAEP analyses.
* Statistically significant difference from 1986 at the .05 level.
Jackknifed standard errors are presented in parentheses.

THE NATION'S REPORT CARD naep

Hispanic students showed recent improvements. The timing of these improvements reflected national trends, with the performance of 13-year-olds improving primarily between 1978 and 1982, and that of 17-year-olds improving primarily between 1982 and 1986.

At ages 9 and 13, the performance of White students was relatively level across the 13-year period from 1973 to 1986. At age 17, performance mirrored national trends, first declining between 1973 and 1982, and then improving significantly between 1982 and 1986.

FIGURE 1.2

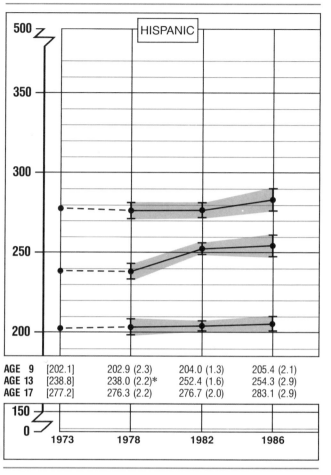

AGE 9	[202.1]	202.9 (2.3)	204.0 (1.3)	205.4 (2.1)
AGE 13	[238.8]	238.0 (2.2)*	252.4 (1.6)	254.3 (2.9)
AGE 17	[277.2]	276.3 (2.2)	276.7 (2.0)	283.1 (2.9)

95%
CONFIDENCE
INTERVAL

Because performance levels remained relatively constant at ages 9 and 13 for White students, and 17-year-olds appear only to be approaching their previous achievement levels, this majority group did not improve its performance significantly over the 13-year period at any of the three age levels assessed. Therefore, the gains made by Black students at all three ages and by Hispanic students (particularly at age 13) served to narrow the performance gaps appreciably. However, achievement of Black and Hispanic students is still well below that of White students at all three age levels and remains a major concern. Programs designed to improve the mathematics proficiency of these minority youth should continue to be a high priority for educators and policymakers alike.

While NAEP does not have trend data for Asian-American students, a discussion of performance for racial/ethnic subpopulations would not be complete without highlighting the comparatively high performance of Asian-American students at all three grade levels assessed by NAEP. TABLE 1.1 displays the 1986 assessment results for White, Black, Hispanic, and Asian-American students in grades 3, 7, and 11. As indicated by the large measurement error, Asian-American students comprise only a very small proportion of the sample assessed by NAEP (less than two percent), and interpretations should be made with caution. However, it appears that Asian-American students performed well above Black and Hispanic students at all three grade levels. Although performance levels for White and Asian-American students appear comparable at grade 3, Asian-American students outperformed their White peers at both grades 7 and 11.

Mathematics Proficiency for White, Black, Hispanic, and Asian-American Students in Grades 3, 7, and 11: 1986*			TABLE 1.1
	Grade 3	**Grade 7**	**Grade 11**
White Students	219.7 (0.8)	274.0 (0.6)	309.4 (0.7)
Black Students	187.8 (1.5)	245.4 (0.8)	279.2 (1.2)
Hispanic Students	194.6 (1.7)	251.3 (1.1)	285.6 (1.5)
Asian-American Students	211.3 (3.8)	288.6 (3.8)	330.6 (5.3)

*Jackknifed standard errors are presented in parentheses.

Trends by Gender

Although trends in average proficiency look remarkably similar across gender, there have been some subtle shifts. In 1986, 9-year-old girls and boys had identical average mathematics proficiency. However, this represented recent significant gains since 1978 for boys but not for girls. A similar pattern emerged for the 13-year-olds. In 1986, average performance was about the same for boys and girls, but this represented a significant improvement from 1978 for the boys and comparatively consistent performance across assessments for the girls (FIGURE 1.3).

Trends in Average Mathematics Proficiency for
9-, 13-, and 17-Year-Olds by Gender: 1973-1986

FIGURE 1.3

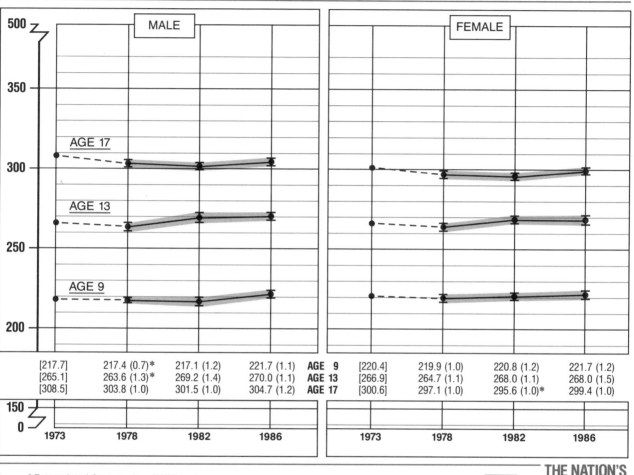

[217.7]	217.4 (0.7)*	217.1 (1.2)	221.7 (1.1)	**AGE 9**	[220.4]	219.9 (1.0)	220.8 (1.2)	221.7 (1.2)
[265.1]	263.6 (1.3)*	269.2 (1.4)	270.0 (1.1)	**AGE 13**	[266.9]	264.7 (1.1)	268.0 (1.1)	268.0 (1.5)
[308.5]	303.8 (1.0)	301.5 (1.0)	304.7 (1.2)	**AGE 17**	[300.6]	297.1 (1.0)	295.6 (1.0)*	299.4 (1.0)

[- - -] Extrapolated from previous NAEP analyses.
* Statistically significant difference from 1986 at the .05 level.
Jackknifed standard errors are presented in parentheses.

95% CONFIDENCE INTERVAL

THE NATION'S REPORT CARD naep

Although the mathematics achievement of males was higher than that of females in each assessment, trends for the 17-year-olds were in some sense reversed. Consistent with the national trends for 17-year-olds, both males and females showed declines in performance between 1973 and 1982. In 1986, both males and females demonstrated improved performance, but the improvement for the females was statistically significant and the improvement for the males was not. By 1986, gender differences in mathematics performance appeared to be minimal at ages 9 and 13, and only slightly larger at age 17.

Trends in Average Mathematics Proficiency for
9-, 13-, and 17-Year-Olds by Region of the Country: 1973-1986

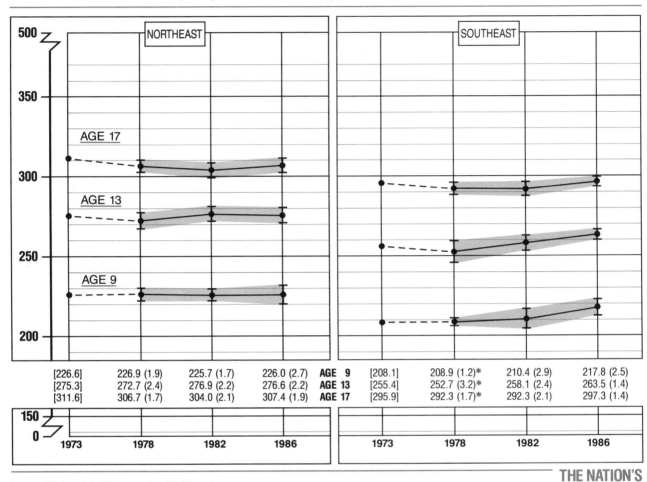

	NORTHEAST					SOUTHEAST		
[226.6]	226.9 (1.9)	225.7 (1.7)	226.0 (2.7)	**AGE 9**	[208.1]	208.9 (1.2)*	210.4 (2.9)	217.8 (2.5)
[275.3]	272.7 (2.4)	276.9 (2.2)	276.6 (2.2)	**AGE 13**	[255.4]	252.7 (3.2)*	258.1 (2.4)	263.5 (1.4)
[311.6]	306.7 (1.7)	304.0 (2.1)	307.4 (1.9)	**AGE 17**	[295.9]	292.3 (1.7)*	292.3 (2.1)	297.3 (1.4)

| 1973 | 1978 | 1982 | 1986 | 1973 | 1978 | 1982 | 1986 |

[– – –] Extrapolated from previous NAEP analyses.
* Statistically significant difference from 1986 at the .05 level.
Jackknifed standard errors are presented in parentheses.

THE NATION'S
REPORT
CARD

Trends by Region

Regional trends for NAEP's four mathematics assessments are presented in FIGURE 1.4. (See Procedural Appendix for definition of regions.) At ages 13 and 17, regional trends uniformly declined between 1973 and 1978. At age 9, performance was relatively stable. From 1978 to 1986, the Southeast was the only region to show significant improvement at all three ages assessed. Although 13-year-olds in the West also improved significantly during this same eight-year period, the remaining regional trends indicate fluctuations but no significant changes.

26

FIGURE 1.4

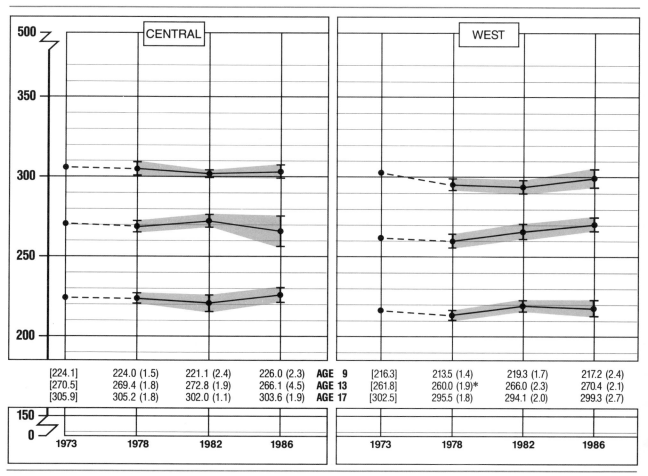

	1973	1978	1982	1986			1973	1978	1982	1986
	[224.1]	224.0 (1.5)	221.1 (2.4)	226.0 (2.3)	**AGE 9**		[216.3]	213.5 (1.4)	219.3 (1.7)	217.2 (2.4)
	[270.5]	269.4 (1.8)	272.8 (1.9)	266.1 (4.5)	**AGE 13**		[261.8]	260.0 (1.9)*	266.0 (2.3)	270.4 (2.1)
	[305.9]	305.2 (1.8)	302.0 (1.1)	303.6 (1.9)	**AGE 17**		[302.5]	295.5 (1.8)	294.1 (2.0)	299.3 (2.7)

95%
CONFIDENCE
INTERVAL

It is worth highlighting recent improvements in the Southeastern region, as the efforts expended toward educational reform throughout the Southern states are well documented.[5] Enhanced teacher training programs, career incentives, expanded assessment programs, increased graduation requirements, strict monitoring of absenteeism, increased amounts of homework,

[5]Denis Doyle and Terry Hartle, *Excellence in Education: The States Take Charge*. American Enterprise Institute, 1985.

27

and heightened citizen awareness all mark the movement toward academic excellence in the South and these efforts appear to have been beneficial. As the Southeast improves and the other regions remain relatively stable, the differences in performance levels among the regions are becoming increasingly negligible.

Summary

The results of the 1986 NAEP mathematics assessment indicate recent improvements in the mathematics proficiency of America's young people. At age 17, achievement increased between 1982 and 1986, suggesting initial recovery from the pervasive declines of the 1970s. At age 9, the first appreciable improvements in achievement since 1973 were shown during this same time period. At age 13, student performance improved between 1978 and 1982, but leveled off in 1986. As a consequence of these increases at the two younger age levels, both groups of students showed significant gains during the eight-year period between 1978 and 1986.

The trends in average mathematics proficiency were encouraging for subpopulations of students generally considered to be at-risk, and these improvements appreciably narrowed differences in performance among demographic subpopulations. White students tended to show only slight increases in performance between 1978 and 1986, but Black students improved significantly at all three age levels. Hispanic students also tended to improve during this same time period, although less dramatically. The only region to show significant improvement in mathematics proficiency across assessments was the Southeast.

Data from the 1986 assessment showed that Asian-American students outperformed all other racial/ethnic groups including White students at grades 7 and 11. It also indicated that performance levels were about the same for boys and girls at ages 9 and 13. However, at age 17, the mathematical proficiency of males was higher than that of females.

The only region to show significant improvement in mathematics proficiency across assessments was the Southeast.

28

CHAPTER 2
What Can
Students Do?

Levels of Mathematics Proficiency
for the Nation and Demographic Subgroups

Defining Levels of Proficiency

NAEP has
defined five
levels of mathe-
matics profi-
ciency based on
a retrospective
analysis of the
assessment
results.

RECENT CALLS for reform in mathematics education, a reaction to continuing poor performance in the 1970s, address the need to increase both average performance *and* the percentage of students reaching the higher ranges of proficiency. The recent improvement at age 9 as well as the signs of recovery at ages 13 and 17 are heartening and indicate some progress toward the first goal.

To describe more precisely the nature of mathematics performance and to document progress toward the second goal, that of helping more students reach the higher ranges of proficiency, NAEP has defined five levels of mathematics proficiency based on a retrospective analysis of the assessment results.

Using the range of student performance on the NAEP mathematics scale summarized in Chapter 1, five levels of mathematics proficiency were established: Level 150—Simple Arithmetic Facts, Level 200—Beginning Skills and Understanding, Level 250—Basic Operations and Beginning Problem Solving, Level 300—Moderately Complex Procedures and Reasoning, and Level 350—Multi-step Problem Solving and Algebra. Although proficiency levels above and below this range can theoretically be defined, few students in the NAEP sample performed at the extreme ends of the scale—that is, from 0 to 150 and from 350 to 500—and therefore any attempt to define other levels would have been highly speculative.

Benchmark questions were assigned to each proficiency level, based on the probability of correct responses. (Please refer to the Procedural Appendix for a more elaborate discussion of the methods used to define proficiency levels.) Mathematics educators analyzed the empirically selected items and characterized the requisite skills held by students performing at each of the five levels of proficiency. Three factors appeared to affect performance: 1) the kind of mathematical operation students were asked to perform, 2) the type of numbers or number system involved, and 3) the problem situation. Students had less difficulty with basic operations, whole numbers, and straightforward problem settings. As the operations grew more involved and the problems moved out of the realm of whole numbers, performance levels decreased. Similarly, students had more difficulty with questions requiring the application of concepts, particularly in non-routine situations. FIGURE 2.1 provides a summary of the levels and their characteristic skills.

As the operations grew more involved and the problems moved out of the realm of whole numbers, performance levels decreased.

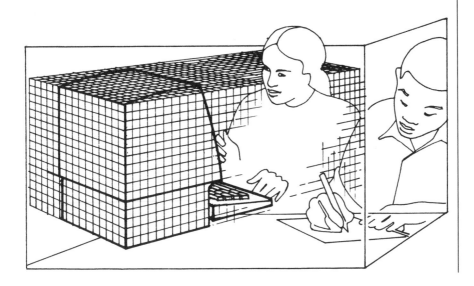

Levels of Mathematics Proficiency

FIGURE 2.1

Level 150—Simple Arithmetic Facts

Learners at this level know some basic addition and subtraction facts, and most can add two-digit numbers without regrouping. They recognize simple situations in which addition and subtraction apply. They also are developing rudimentary classification skills.

Level 200—Beginning Skills and Understanding

Learners at this level have considerable understanding of two-digit numbers. They can add two-digit numbers, but are still developing an ability to regroup in subtraction. They know some basic multiplication and division facts, recognize relations among coins, can read information from charts and graphs, and use simple measurement instruments. They are developing some reasoning skills.

Level 250—Basic Operations and Beginning Problem Solving

Learners at this level have an initial understanding of the four basic operations. They are able to apply whole number addition and subtraction skills to one-step word problems and money situations. In multiplication, they can find the product of a two-digit and a one-digit number. They can also compare information from graphs and charts, and are developing an ability to analyze simple logical relations.

Level 300—Moderately Complex Procedures and Reasoning

Learners at this level are developing an understanding of number systems. They can compute with decimals, simple fractions, and commonly encountered percents. They can identify geometric figures, measure lengths and angles, and calculate areas of rectangles. These students are also able to interpret simple inequalities, evaluate formulas, and solve simple linear equations. They can find averages, make decisions on information drawn from graphs, and use logical reasoning to solve problems. They are developing the skills to operate with signed numbers, exponents, and square roots.

Level 350—Multi-step Problem Solving and Algebra

Learners at this level can apply a range of reasoning skills to solve multi-step problems. They can solve routine problems involving fractions and percents, recognize properties of basic geometric figures, and work with exponents and square roots. They can solve a variety of two-step problems using variables, identify equivalent algebraic expressions, and solve linear equations and inequalities. They are developing an understanding of functions and coordinate systems.

THE NATION'S REPORT CARD / naep

TABLE 2.1 shows the percentage of students at ages 9, 13, and 17 who attained each level of proficiency in the 1978, 1982, and 1986 assessments. The highest mathematics levels attained across the three assessments by most students in each age group are highlighted, as are the 1986 percentages of 17-year-olds achieving the two highest proficiency levels.

**Trends for 9-, 13-, and 17-Year-Old Students
Percentage of Students at or Above
the Five Proficiency Levels: 1978-1986**

TABLE 2.1

| Proficiency Levels | Age | Assessment Year | | |
		1978	1982	1986
Level 150	9	**96.5** (0.2)	**97.2** (0.3)	**97.8** (0.2)
Simple Arithmetic	13	99.8 (0.0)	99.9 (0.0)	100.0 (0.0)
Facts	17	100.0 (0.0)	100.0 (0.0)	100.0 (0.0)
Level 200	9	70.3 (0.9)*	71.5 (1.1)	73.9 (1.1)
Beginning Skills and	13	**94.5** (0.4)*	**97.6** (0.4)	**98.5** (0.2)
Understandings	17	99.8 (0.0)	99.9 (0.1)	99.9 (0.1)
Level 250	9	19.4 (0.6)	18.7 (0.8)	20.8 (0.9)
Basic Operations and	13	64.9 (1.2)*	71.6 (1.2)	73.1 (1.5)
Beginning Problem Solving	17	**92.1** (0.5)*	**92.9** (0.5)*	**96.0** (0.4)
Level 300	9	0.8 (0.1)	0.6 (0.1)	0.6 (0.2)
Moderately Complex	13	17.9 (0.7)	17.8 (0.9)	15.9 (1.0)
Procedures and Reasoning	17	51.4 (1.1)	48.3 (1.2)	**51.1** (1.2)
Level 350	9	0.0 (0.0)	0.0 (0.0)	0.0 (0.0)
Multi-step Problem	13	0.9 (0.2)	0.5 (0.1)	0.4 (0.1)
Solving and Algebra	17	7.4 (0.4)	5.4 (0.4)	**6.4** (0.4)

*Statistically significant difference from 1986 at the .05 level. (No significance test is reported when the proportion of students is either >95.0 or <5.0.) Jackknifed standard errors are presented in parentheses.

National Trends in Levels of Mathematics Proficiency

LEVEL 150

Simple Arithmetic Facts

1986		
Age 9	Age 13	Age 17
97.8	100.0	100.0

Students performing at or above Level 150 are able to perform elementary addition and subtraction; however, their ability to apply these simple arithmetic procedures is likely to be quite constrained. Two sample items associated with Level 150 performance are provided below.

Which of these numbers is closest to 30?

○   20

●   28

○   34

○   40

Add

```
   35
 + 42
```

ANSWER _77_

In 1986, as in the two previous assessments, virtually all students in each of the three age groups performed at or above Level 150. The results of the 1986 assessment indicate that American educators have been largely successful in their efforts to teach basic arithmetic skills to students in the initial grades.

LEVEL 200

Beginning Skills and Understanding

1986		
Age 9	Age 13	Age 17
73.8	98.5	99.9

Students performing at or above Level 200 are developing a greater range and depth of basic mathematical skills however, their use of these skills is still imperfect and relatively inflexible. It can be inferred that learners at this level would have difficulty with reasoning that requires more than simple numerical computation. Seven sample items representative of Level 200 performance are provided below.

Subtract

$$39 - 26 = \underline{13}$$

$$79 - 45 = \underline{34}$$

Each bag has 10 marbles in it. How many marbles are there in all?

- ○ 10
- ○ 15
- ○ 25
- ○ 140
- ● 150
- ○ 160
- ○ I don't know.

Which coins are the same amount of money as a quarter?

- ○ 2 dimes
- ● 3 nickels and 1 dime
- ○ 3 dimes
- ○ 4 nickels
- ○ I don't know.

Find the quotient.

5⟌15

ANSWER___3___

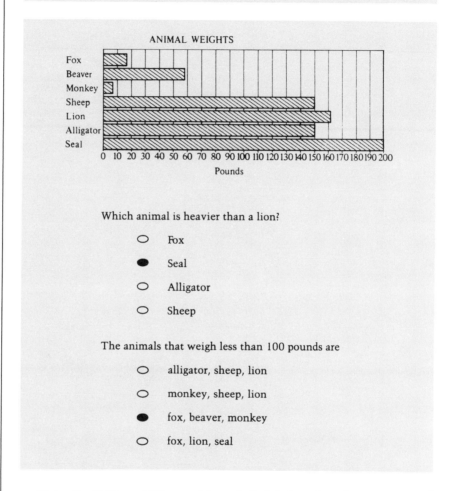

Which animal is heavier than a lion?

- ○ Fox
- ● Seal
- ○ Alligator
- ○ Sheep

The animals that weigh less than 100 pounds are

- ○ alligator, sheep, lion
- ○ monkey, sheep, lion
- ● fox, beaver, monkey
- ○ fox, lion, seal

Virtually all 13- and 17-year-olds, and slightly less than three-quarters of the 9-year-olds, performed at or above Level 200 in the 1986 assessment. This represented significantly improved performance at both ages 9 and 13 between 1978 and 1986, indicating a rise in the proportion of students who have mastered low-level mathematical skills and knowledge.

Although these findings are generally positive, it must still be recognized that 26 percent of 9-year-olds who have not reached Level 200 constitute approximately 700,000 boys and girls in the third and fourth grades who have not yet acquired an understanding of rudimentary mathematical skills and concepts.

Basic Operations
and Beginning Problem Solving

Age 9	Age 13	Age 17
20.8	73.1	96.0

Students performing at or beyond Level 250 on the proficiency scale have developed a surface understanding of the four basic operations, and are beginning to acquire more developed reasoning skills. A series of sample problems indicative of performance at Level 250 is provided below.

Which is worth the most?

○ 11 nickels

● 6 dimes

○ 1 half dollar

○ I don't know

Subtract

604
−207

ANSWER *397*

There are 10 airplanes on the ground. 6 take off and 4 more land. How many are on the ground then?

○ 4

● 8

○ 14

○ 20

At the store, the price of a carton of milk is 40¢, an apple is 25¢, and a box of crackers is 30¢. What is the cost of an apple and a carton of milk?

○ 55¢

● 65¢

○ 70¢

○ 95¢

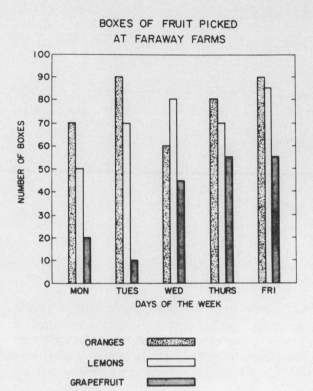

BOXES OF FRUIT PICKED
AT FARAWAY FARMS

ORANGES

LEMONS

GRAPEFRUIT

How many boxes of oranges, lemons, and grapefruit were picked on
Tuesday?

○ 10

○ 90

● 170

○ 400

○ 940

○ 1700

○ I don't know.

Find the product

$$21 \times 3$$

ANSWER___63___

Sam has 68 baseball cards. Juanita has 127. Which number sentence could be used to find how many more cards Juanita has than Sam?

● $127 - 68 = \boxed{}$

○ $127 + \boxed{} = 68$

○ $68 - \boxed{} = 127$

○ $68 + 127 = \boxed{}$

○   I don't know.

At Level 250, substantial differences in performance begin to appear across the age groups. Less than one-quarter of the 9-year-olds reached this level in any of the three most recent assessments. Given that basic computational skills are universally taught in the elementary grades, one would hope to see higher levels of proficiency at age 9 than have been found.

Although significantly more 13-year-olds performed at or above Level 250 in 1986 (73 percent) than in 1978 (65 percent), most of the gain occurred between 1978 and 1982, and the percentage of students achieving this level in either assessment is still quite low. Generalized to the nation as a whole, it is alarming that one-quarter of the seventh and eighth graders—amounting to more than three-quarters of a million students—may not possess the skills in whole-number computation necessary to perform many everyday tasks. The percentage of 17-year-olds performing at or above Level 250 also increased, from about 92 percent in both 1978 and 1982 to 96 percent in 1986. Although nearly all the high school students demonstrated proficiency in basic operations and beginning problem solving, the 4 percent of in-school 17-year-olds who did not reach this level would seem to be at a considerable disadvantage as adults—as would a presumably large proportion of their peers who have dropped out of school.

. . . one-quarter of the seventh and eighth graders— amounting to more than three-quarters of a million students— may not possess the skills in whole-number computation necessary to perform many everyday tasks.

Students performing at or above Level 300 demonstrate more sophisticated numerical reasoning, and are beginning to draw from a wider range of mathematical skill areas, including algebra and geometry. A set of sample items representative of Level 300 performance is provided below.

Which of the following is true about 87% of 10?

- ○ It is greater than 10.
- ● It is less than 10.
- ○ It is equal to 10.
- ○ Can't tell.
- ○ I don't know.

If $7x + 4 = 5x + 8$, then $x =$

- ○ 1
- ● 2
- ○ 4
- ○ 6

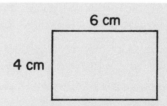

What is the area of this rectangle?

- ○ 4 square cm
- ○ 6 square cm
- ○ 10 square cm
- ○ 20 square cm
- ● 24 square cm
- ○ I don't know.

Refer to the following graph. This graph shows how far a typical car travels after the brakes are applied.

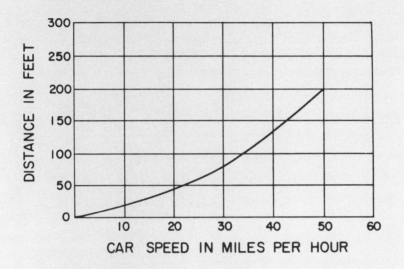

A car is traveling 55 miles per hour. About how far will it travel after applying the brakes?

- ○   25 feet
- ○   200 feet
- ●   240 feet
- ○   350 feet
- ○   I don't know.

In 1986, less than 1 percent of the 9-year-olds, 16 percent of the 13-year-olds, and 51 percent of the 17-year-olds were able to perform at or above this level. Further, at age 13, this reflects a decrease from the 1978 and 1982 assessments.

Although the knowledge and problem-solving skills required to answer items at Level 300 are too advanced for 9-year-olds, it is troubling that more 13- and 17-year-olds have not attained this level of performance. Given that students are exposed to many of these topics in middle and junior high school, one would expect to see a higher percentage of students at age 13 and particularly at age 17 demonstrating success at this level of proficiency. The finding seems to lend support to recent calls for more challenging curriculum in the middle and upper grades.

The finding seems to lend support to recent calls for more challenging curriculum in the middle and upper grades.

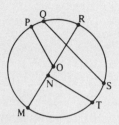

Which of the following is a radius of the circle?

● $\overline{OP}$

○ $\overline{QS}$

○ $\overline{RM}$

○ $\overline{NT}$

Which points are the end points of an arc?

○ O, P

● Q, S

○ N, T

○ N, M

Educating Americans for the 21st Century recommended that *all* secondary school students should achieve a variety of mathematics outcomes, including an understanding of the logic behind algebraic manipulations, a knowledge of two- and three-dimensional figures and their properties, and some more advanced objectives.[1] These recommendations were made to raise American secondary students' achievement so that it would be the best in the world by 1995. The performance data for Level 300 items in the NAEP mathematics assessment indicate that we have a great distance to go before our students achieve the levels defined by these recommendations.

Further, the fact that nearly half of the 17-year-olds do not have mathematical skills beyond basic computation with whole numbers has serious implications. With such limited mathematical abilities, these students nearing graduation are unlikely to be able to match mathematical tools to the demands of various problem situations that permeate life and work.

---

[1]*Educating Americans for the 21st Century: A Plan of Action for Improving Mathematics, Science and Technology Education for All American Elementary and Secondary Students So That Their Achievement Is the Best in the World by 1995.* A Report to the American People and the National Science Board, the National Science Board Commission on Precollege Education in Mathematics, Science, and Technology, 1983.

LEVEL 350

Multi-step Problem Solving and Algebra

1986

Age 9	Age 13	Age 17
0.0	0.4	6.4

Students performing at Level 350 demonstrate the capacity to apply mathematical operations in a variety of problem settings. A set of sample items representative of this level of performance is provided below.

R	S	40
35	25	15
T	V	W

In the figure above, R, S, T, V, and W represent numbers. The figure is called a magic square because adding the numbers in any row or column or diagonal results in the same sum. What is the value of R?

- ● 30
- ○ 40
- ○ 50
- ○ Can't tell

Suppose you have 10 coins and have at least one each of a quarter, a dime, a nickel, and a penny. What is the <u>least</u> amount of money you could have?

- ○ 41¢
- ● 47¢
- ○ 50¢
- ○ 82¢

If $f(x) = x^3 - x^2 + x - 4$, what is $f(-3)$?

- ● −43
- ○ −37
- ○ −1
- ○ 17

Christine borrowed $850 for one year from the Friendly Finance Company. If she paid 12% simple interest on the loan, what was the total amount she repaid?

ANSWER $952

Which of the following are equivalent equations?

- ○ $x + 2 = 9$ and $x - 2 = 9$
- ● $y - 3 = 7$ and $y + 5 = 15$
- ○ $z - 6 = 3$ and $z = 3$
- ○ $1 + 2 = w$ and $w + 1 = 2$

The number of tomato plants (t) is twice the number of pepper plants (p). Which equation best describes the sentence above?

- ● $t = 2p$
- ○ $2t = p$
- ○ $t = 2 + p$
- ○ $2 + t = p$

$\sqrt{17}$ is between which of the following pairs of numbers?

- ● 4 and 5
- ○ 8 and 9
- ○ 16 and 18
- ○ 288 and 290
- ○ I don't know.

Virtually no 9- or 13-year-olds and only a small proportion of 17-year-olds (6 percent) attained Level 350 performance in the 1986 assessment. Additionally troublesome is the fact that the percentage of students achieving at this level has remained essentially constant since 1978. At a time when mathematical and scientific skills are in high demand in the labor force, few students in their latter years of high school have mastered the fundamentals needed to perform more advanced mathematical operations.

43

Levels of Mathematics Proficiency
for Demographic Subgroups

That most students fail to reach the higher levels of mathematics proficiency is sufficient cause for educators' concern. But how are special populations faring? A comparison of the mathematical abilities of various demographic subgroups with each other and with the nation as a whole offers a way to study variations in performance across subpopulations of interest. The populations of particular interest in this report are those distinguished by race, gender and region. (See Procedural Appendix for definitions.)

Levels of Proficiency by Race/Ethnicity

Essentially all students at ages 9, 13, and 17 performed at or above Level 150 in the 1986 assessment. However, even as early as age 9, there was slight variation across racial/ethnic groups in the percentage of students attaining this lowest level of proficiency. As illustrated in FIGURE 2.2, a smaller percentage of Black and Hispanic 9-year-olds performed at Level 150 than did White students in this age group.

At all higher levels of proficiency, as well, White students consistently outperformed Hispanic students, and Hispanic students consistently outperformed Black students (with the single exception of 17-year-olds performing at Level 200). Disparities were especially striking among 9-year-olds at Level 200, among 13-year-olds at Level 250, and among 17-year-olds at Level 300. Thus, as age and level of proficiency increased, so did the performance gaps between racial/ethnic subpopulations.

Although these findings are discouraging, trends in levels of mathematics proficiency indicate considerable progress over the last eight years for racial/ethnic minorities. Unfortunately, as in the trends for the population at large, most of the increases occurred in the lower range of proficiency, primarily at Levels 200 and 250. (Please refer to Data Appendix for trend data.)

> Thus, as age and level of proficiency increased, so did the performance gaps between racial/ethnic subpopulations.

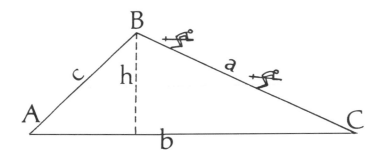

44

Levels of Mathematics Proficiency: Percent at or Above Anchor Points by Race/Ethnicity: 1986

FIGURE 2.2

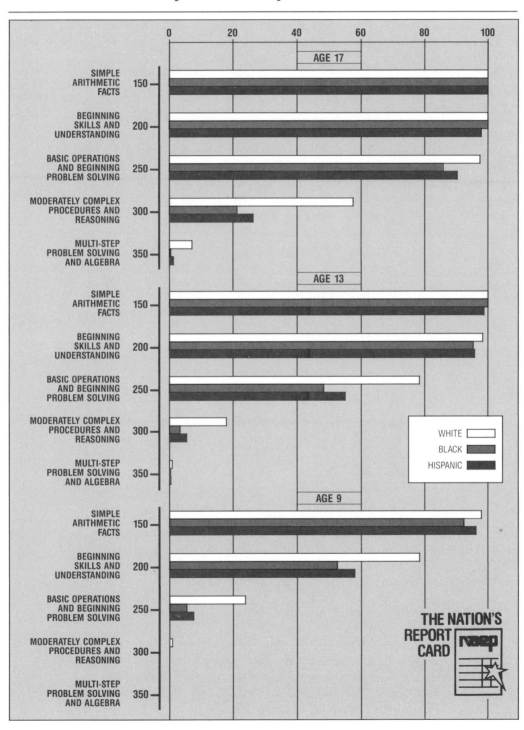

Levels of Proficiency by Gender

Within each age group, roughly the same percentages of males and females had mathematics proficiency at Level 150 or 200, as depicted in FIGURE 2.3. However, variations began to appear among 13- and 17-year-olds who achieved at or beyond Level 250. Differences were particularly evident among 13-year-olds at Level 300, and among 17-year-olds at Levels 300 and 350, with more males achieving these higher levels than females.

Trends over time indicate that an increased proportion of both males and females attained Levels 150 to 250 from 1978 to 1986, and that the small gender performance gaps that existed at these levels in the 1978 and 1982 assessments have been further diminished. In the same time period, the proportions of both males and females achieving at Levels 300 and 350 have increased only slightly, and while there are still fewer females than males at both levels of proficiency, the performance gaps between the genders have not changed considerably.

Levels of Proficiency by Region

In examining the 1986 assessment results by region, it appears that differences across the four regions—Northeast, Southeast, Central, and West—are greatest at the upper levels of proficiency, primarily at Levels 250, 300, and 350. FIGURE 2.4 provides a comparative view of the levels of proficiency attained by students from each of these regions.

Although students from the Northeast, Central, and West regions were generally more likely than students from the Southeast region to attain Levels 200 to 350, trend data indicate that the latter group has made considerable progress since the 1978 assessment. For students from the Southeast, significant increases were evident from 1978 to 1986 in the percentage of both 9- and 13-year-olds performing at Level 200, and in the percentage of 17-year-olds performing at Level 250.

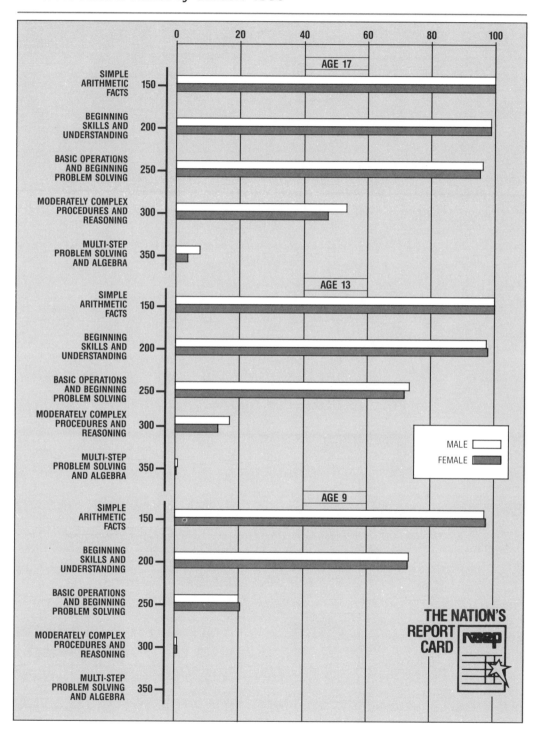

FIGURE 2.4

Levels of Mathematics Proficiency: Percent at or Above Anchor Points by Region: 1986

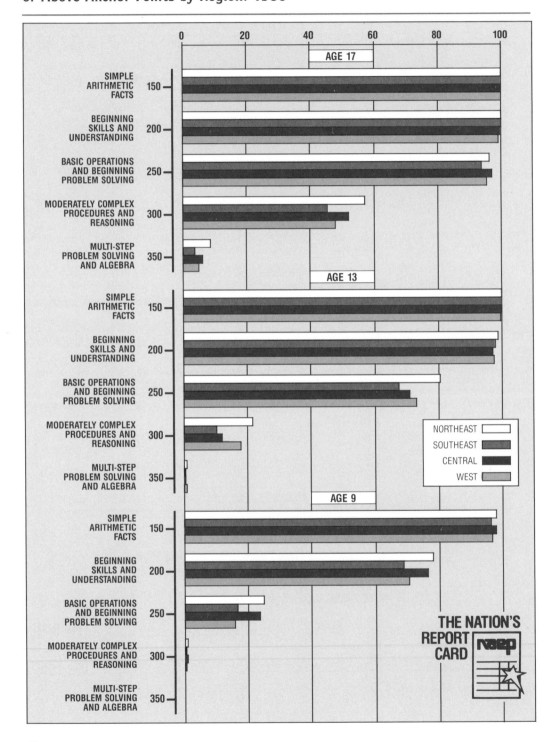

THE NATION'S REPORT CARD

48

Summary

As documented in Chapter 1, the mathematical performance of students at ages 9, 13, and 17 has improved somewhat over the past eight years, yet a closer look at levels of proficiency indicates that most of the progress has occurred in the domain of lower-order skills.

The more detailed account of what students can and cannot do at each level of proficiency gives further weight to educators' concerns that many students lack skills commonly thought to be mastered at the elementary, middle, and high school levels. It appears that the discrepancy between students' expected and actual mathematics performance begins early on in schooling, and increases as they move into the upper grades. One would expect a majority of 9-year-olds (primarily fourth graders) to have mastered basic mathematical operations and beginning problem solving (at Level 250), as these skills are usually taught in elementary school. The fact that only 21 percent of the 9-year-olds attained this level in the 1986 assessment and that one-quarter of them failed to demonstrate even beginning skills and understanding (Level 200) suggests that reform in the mathematics curriculum may be warranted from the earliest grades.

At age 13, the discrepancy between students' expected and actual proficiency is larger still. Moderately complex mathematical procedures and reasoning (at Level 300) generally are embedded throughout the middle and junior high school curriculum, yet in 1986 only 16 percent of the students assessed at age 13 demonstrated a grasp of these skills. It seems likely that children who did not receive a strong mathematics foundation in the elementary grades have increasing difficulty in the subject through their middle years of schooling, as more difficult operations and concepts are introduced.

The discrepancy between expected and actual performance grows even more pronounced among 17-year-olds, of whom only 6 percent in the 1986 assessment displayed abilities in multi-step problem solving and algebra (at Level 350). Only about half of the 17-year-olds demonstrated even a moderately complex understanding of mathematics, as exemplified by Level 300 performance. Translated into population figures, nearly 1.5 million 17-year-old students across the nation appear scarcely able to perform the kinds of numerical operations that will likely be required of them in future life and work settings.

These concerns are heightened by the fact that the 17-year-olds sampled in the fourth mathematics assessment did not include the 14 percent of the cohort who have already dropped out of school by junior year.[2] It is quite likely that the mathematical proficiency of these absent students is consider-

. . . children who did not receive a strong mathematics foundation in the elementary grades have increasing difficulty in the subject through their middle years of schooling . . .

[2] *The Condition of Education, 1984 Edition.* National Center for Education Statistics (NCES), 1985.

49

ably lower; hence the 1.5-million figure quoted previously would be optimistic for the entire 17-year-old population.

For subpopulations whose mathematics performance has tended to lie below national averages in NAEP assessments—including Black and Hispanic students and residents of the Southeast—the discrepancy between expected and actual performance for all age groups remains even larger than that for the nation as a whole, despite considerable gains in recent years.

The levels of proficiency exhibited by American students, particularly in the higher age groups, are likely to be inadequate for the demands of the times. A nation that wants to continue to reap the benefits of modern technology and to compete in the future global economy depends on the skills of the young, and it appears that our students are ill-prepared to meet these challenges.

CHAPTER 3
Beyond Computation?

Relative Strengths and Weaknesses Across Mathematics Content Areas for the Nation and Subpopulations at Grades 3, 7, and 11

T HIS CHAPTER contains information on students' relative performance in particular mathematics content areas. The topics covered in NAEP's 1986 mathematics assessment were drawn from typical elementary and secondary school mathematics curricula up to but not including calculus, and the questions were developed to address broad areas designated in the booklet, *Math Objectives: 1985-86 Assessment.* Based on this design, NAEP was able to compute results for five different mathematics content area subscales: *Knowledge and Skills in Numbers and Operations, Higher-Level Applications in Numbers and Operations, Measurement, Geometry,* and *Algebra.* Descriptions of these content areas are presented in FIGURE 3.1.

Descriptions of the Content Areas Represented by the NAEP Mathematics Subscales

FIGURE 3.1

Knowledge and Skills in Numbers and Operations. This subscale spanning all three grade levels—third, seventh, and eleventh—is based on items measuring students' knowledge (recognition and recall) of words, symbols, and figures and their skills in performing straightforward, routine manipulations. They are able to use standard computational procedures with whole numbers, common fractions, decimals, and percents.

Higher-Level Applications in Numbers and Operations. Also spanning the three grade levels, this subscale measures a deeper understanding of the concepts, assumptions, and relationships between and among whole numbers, fractions, decimals, and percents as well as the operations associated with them. In addition to their knowledge, skills, and understanding, students use such problem-solving processes as identifying and implementing an appropriate strategy, screening relevant from irrelevant information, or recognizing patterns and describing or symbolizing the relationships.

Measurement. The third scale spanning all three grade levels is based on developmental concepts of measurement, equivalent measurements, and instrument reading (e.g., length, time, temperature, mass/weight, area, volume, capacity, angles, as well as applications to circles, scale drawings, and money).

Geometry. This scale spans the two higher grade levels and includes the properties and relations of geometric figures (i.e., parallel lines, perpendicular lines, similar polygons, congruent figures, angles of triangle, etc.), lines of symmetry, images of figures, and other spatial relations in two and three dimensions.

Algebra—Relations, Functions, and Algebraic Expressions. Because of its place in the curricula, this subscale is only defined for the high-school students. Broad in scope, it includes using variables to express relationships and to represent properties of operations, translations, number theory concepts, determining solutions of equations and inequalities, and functions.

THE NATION'S
REPORT
CARD **naep**

Relative Increases in Performance in Content Areas Across Grade Levels

The mathematics subscales themselves are arbitrary and their meaning in absolute terms is not known—for example, how much learning in measurement equals the same amount of learning in geometry. But they do indicate growth in particular content areas as students progress through school. FIGURE 3.2 indicates relative increases in average proficiency on three of the subscales—knowledge and skills in numbers and operations, higher-level applications in numbers and operations, and measurement—for students in grades 3, 7, and 11.

Average Mathematics Proficiency in Content Area Subscales Across Grades 3, 7, and 11 for the Nation: 1986

FIGURE 3.2

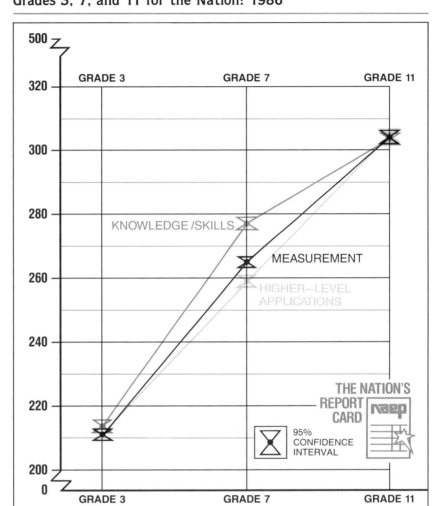

In order to anchor any scale, some points must be fixed. NAEP chose to anchor the points on the mathematics subscales so they would be approximately the same at grades 3 and 11. (Refer to Procedural Appendix for details.) This allowed the results for grade 7 to vary. The findings are revealing: From grade 3 to grade 7, the largest relative increase in performance occurred on the knowledge and skills subscale.

In the NAEP scaling metric, the increase in performance on the higher-level applications subscale was about the same from grades 3 to 7 and from grades 7 to 11—48 and 45 points, respectively. In comparison, for the knowledge and skills subscale, the increase was significantly sharper between grades 3 and 7, but performance leveled off between grades 7 and 11. The finding for the measurement subscale was somewhere in between, increasing slightly more between grades 3 and 7 than higher-level applications and somewhat less than knowledge and skills, before leveling off from grades 7 to 11.

This indicates that students are acquiring arithmetic knowledge and procedures at a rapid pace in the elementary schools, presumably paving the way for the study of algebra, geometry, and other more complex mathematical content in the middle grades and high school. While the way may be paved, the proficiency level results presented in Chapter 2 suggest that most students do not have a grasp of these content areas. Very few students attained the higher levels of mathematics proficiency (300 and 350) characterized by even moderate understanding of geometry or algebra.[1]

As supported by the subscale results, the seventh graders have come much closer to the eleventh-grade level in their knowledge and skills in numbers and operations than they have in their understanding of higher-level applications; a finding that also dominated the relative performance across subscales for racial/ethnic groups, regions, and gender.

The relatively large growth in knowledge and skills between grades 3 and 7 may reflect a general overemphasis in contemporary curricula on computation-related skills or the tendency to teach skills and knowledge before integrating applications and problem solving into instruction. Whatever the explanation for this finding, it would be a mistake to conclude that increased emphasis on lower-level skills and knowledge alone is the appropriate way to help students progress from one level of mathematical proficiency to the next. Rather, students need to simultaneously broaden both their repertoire of problem-solving strategies as well as their knowledge base and conceptual understanding.

Mathematics Content Area Results by Gender

The difference in performance between males and females on tests of spatial abilities is well-documented.[2] The NAEP results confirm this gender difference, showing a consistent advantage for males on the geometry scale at grades 7 and 11 and on the measurement scale at all three grade levels (FIGURE 3.3). These differences are statistically significant at grades 3 and 11, but not at grade 7. It is of interest that NAEP science assessment results

---

[1]Because of the need to arbitrarily anchor the subscales, and because only one or two grade levels are involved, the results for the geometry and algebra subscales cannot be used to illuminate this hypothesis.

[2]Torsten Husen (Ed.), *International Study of Achievement in Mathematics*. Vol. 2. New York: Wiley, 1967.

Eleanor Maccoby, "Sex Differences in Intellectual Functioning." In E. E. Maccoby (Ed.), *The Development of Sex Differences*. Stanford, CA: Stanford University Press, 1966.

FIGURE 3.3

Average Mathematics Proficiency in Content Area Subscales by Gender at Grades 3, 7, and 11: 1986

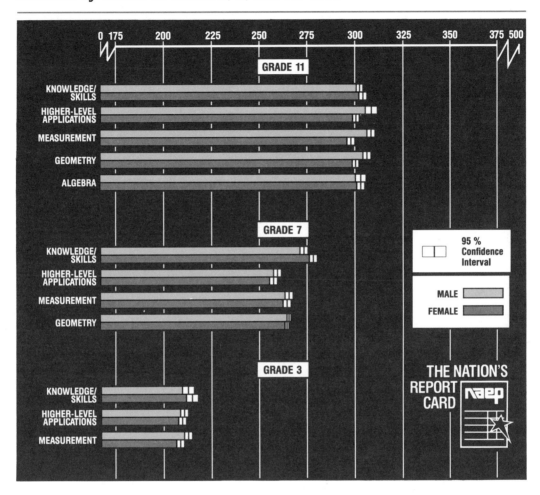

across the years indicate that boys have more experience with measuring instruments than do girls. The discrepancy in childhood experiences also has an effect on the results.[3]

The gender disparities on the two numbers and operations subscales also support existing research findings about differences in the cognitive styles of males and females in mathematics.[4] Females tend to outperform males on tasks where there is an obvious procedural rule to follow, while the reverse

[3]Stacey Hueftle, Steven Rakow, and Wayne Welch, *Images of Science: A Summary of Results from the 1981-82 National Assessment in Science*. Science Assessment and Research Project, University of Minnesota, June 1983.

[4]Sandra Marshall, "Sex Differences in Children's Mathematics Achievement: Solving Computations and Story Problems." *Journal of Education Psychology*, Vol. 76, No. 2, pp 194-204, 1984.

seems to be true when the strategy for solving the problem is less apparent. At all three grade levels, the NAEP results show a consistent advantage for females in the area of knowledge and skills compared to a consistent advantage for males in the area of higher-level applications.

The algebra subscale results do not show any gender differences.

Mathematics Content Area Results by Region

Regional differences in performance on the five content area subscales are presented in FIGURE 3.4. These differences were minimal on the knowledge and skills subscale at all three grade levels, although the Northeast tended toward higher performance at the two upper grade levels. While students in the Central region did best in higher-level applications at grade 3, particularly compared to the West and Southeast, students in the Northeast did significantly better than the other three regions at grade 7 and tended to maintain this advantage at grade 11. Both the Northeast and Central areas of the country performed better than the other two regions in measurement, particularly at the two lower grade levels. In algebra and geometry, the Northeast showed significantly higher proficiency levels than the other three regions, while the Southeast tended to lag behind, particularly at the high-school level.

Mathematics Content Area Results by Race/Ethnicity

At grade 3, the results by racial/ethnic groups are similar for the two subscales based on numbers and operations (FIGURE 3.5). For both knowledge and skills as well as higher-level applications, the White and Asian-American students performed significantly better than the Hispanic students, who tended to perform significantly better than the Black students. White students also performed significantly better than the other groups in measurement.

At grades 7 and 11, the significant advantage in overall performance shown by Asian-American students prevailed across all five content areas. On all subscales, they showed significantly higher proficiency levels than White students, who showed significantly higher levels of performance than either Hispanic or Black students. Hispanic students tended to lose their grade 3 advantage over Black students in knowledge and skills at the two upper grade levels. However, at grades 7 and 11 they performed significantly better than Black students in higher-level applications, measurement, and geometry. Black and Hispanic high-school students showed similar levels of proficiency in algebra.

At all three grade levels, the NAEP results show a consistent advantage for females in the area of knowledge and skills compared to a consistent advantage for males in the area of higher-level applications.

. . . the Northeast showed significantly higher proficiency levels than the other three regions . . .

56

FIGURE 3.4

Average Mathematics Proficiency in Content Area Subscales by Region at Grades 3, 7, and 11: 1986

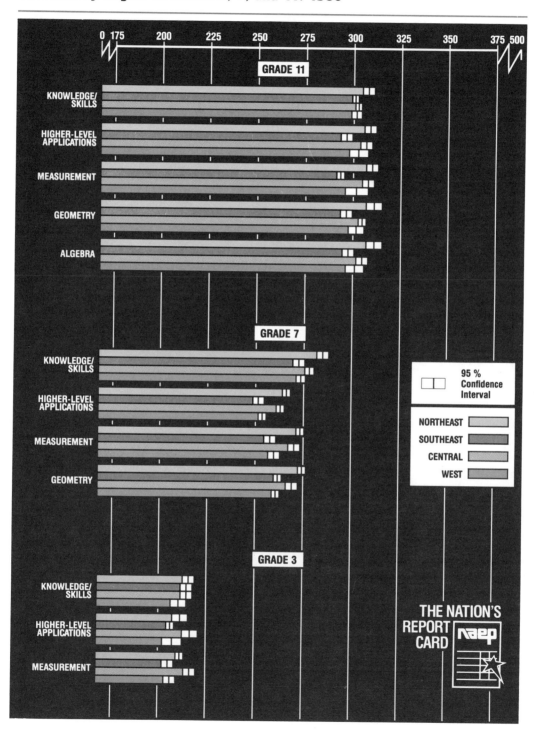

FIGURE 3.5

Average Mathematics Proficiency in Content Area Subscales by Race/Ethnicity at Grades 3, 7, and 11: 1986

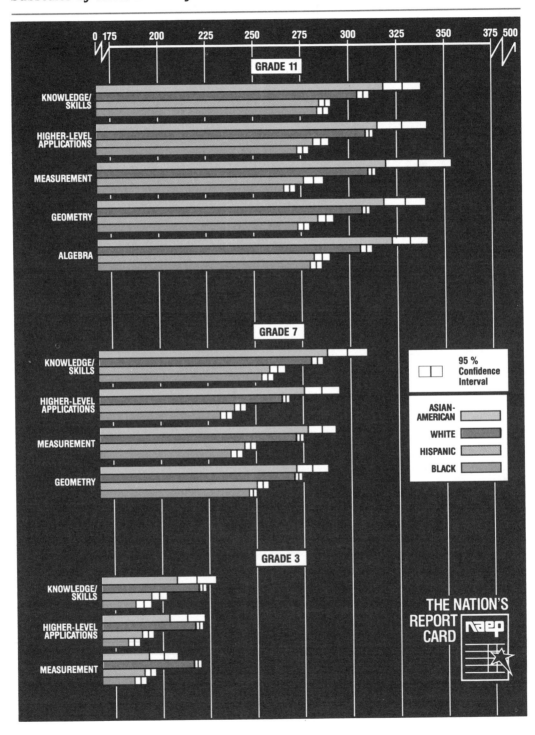

The Effect of High School Course Taking on Content Area Proficiency Levels

A natural question to ask about the relative differences in performance across content areas centers on the impact of course taking. Are differences in performance smaller between groups if they have all had the benefit of focused instruction in a particular content area? TABLE 3.1 presents the average proficiency levels on the geometry and algebra subscales for high-school students who reported having taken those specific courses.

Not surprisingly, the average proficiency levels in geometry were dramatically higher for those eleventh-grade students who had taken geometry. However, in several instances the differences in geometry performance increased between subpopulations when students studied the subject. Although the same percentage (63 percent) of both males and females reported having taken geometry, a four-point difference between proficiency levels for males and females who had not taken geometry doubled for those who had taken geometry. A similar pattern occurred for Hispanic and Black students compared to White students, but to a lesser degree. The relative regional standings tended to be very similar both for students who had taken the course and those who had not.

Overall, completion of second-year algebra had an equally dramatic impact on proficiency levels in algebra. As with geometry, the difference in algebra proficiency levels was larger between White and Hispanic eleventh graders who had taken second-year algebra than between those groups of students who had not. Also, the regional differences were very similar for both groups of students. However, males and females who had taken this course had very similar proficiency levels in that content area, while females performed slightly better among those who had not.

Average Proficiency Scores for Geometry and Algebra Content Area Subscales by Course-Taking in Geometry and Algebra II for Grade 11: 1986*	TABLE 3.1

Population	Geometry Proficiency Scores		
	Percent Having Taken Course	Proficiency Level Have Taken Course	Proficiency Level Have Not Taken Course
Nation	63 (1.1)	321 (0.7)	280 (0.6)
Male	63 (1.6)	325 (0.9)	282 (0.8)
Female	63 (1.0)	317 (0.9)	278 (0.9)
White	66 (1.2)	324 (0.6)	284 (0.7)
Hispanic	47 (2.8)	307 (2.3)	274 (1.3)
Black	48 (2.8)	297 (1.4)	264 (1.0)
Northeast	74 (2.1)	324 (1.3)	280 (1.5)
Central	63 (2.6)	322 (0.6)	282 (1.2)
West	58 (2.4)	320 (1.9)	281 (1.1)
Southeast	55 (2.4)	316 (1.4)	275 (1.2)
	Algebra Proficiency Scores		
Nation	50 (1.2)	326 (0.8)	285 (0.7)
Male	51 (1.4)	326 (1.1)	284 (1.1)
Female	49 (1.3)	325 (1.0)	287 (0.8)
White	53 (1.2)	328 (0.8)	289 (0.9)
Hispanic	35 (1.7)	310 (2.4)	276 (2.0)
Black	37 (2.4)	306 (1.7)	273 (1.6)
Northeast	60 (2.2)	328 (1.6)	289 (2.0)
Central	46 (2.2)	327 (1.2)	288 (1.5)
West	46 (2.5)	325 (2.4)	285 (1.1)
Southeast	46 (2.8)	321 (1.4)	280 (1.3)

*Jackknifed standard errors are presented in parentheses.

Summary

From grades 3 to 7, students appear to be learning basic computational skills at a more rapid pace than they are learning applications of those skills. Across several mathematics content areas, the largest relative increase in performance from grade 3 to grades 7 and 11 occurred on the knowledge and skills subscale from grade 3 to grade 7. The elementary school concentration in this content area could be expected to pave the way for students to learn more complex material in the middle grades and high school. Unfortunately, the descriptions of what older students know and can do in mathematics belie this theory.

The results for demographic subpopulations defined by race/ethnicity, region, and gender tend to follow national patterns across subscales. However, some interesting variations did occur. For example, the results for gender served to reinforce existing research findings about differences in spatial abilities by showing that females are comparatively weak in measurement and geometry. Not only did geometry course-taking not help reduce the difference in proficiency levels at grade 11, but it appeared to have an opposite effect. In the domain of numbers and operations, females showed superior performance compared to males in knowledge and skills, but weaker performance in higher-level applications of those skills.

The SIMS report criticizes the repetitive nature of mathematics curricula in the United States and the NAEP data seemingly support this concern. Students appear to concentrate too much on computation relative to other skill areas and therefore lack the range of abilities and understandings necessary to take advantage of advanced course offerings.

The SIMS report criticizes the repetitive nature of mathematics curricula in the United States and the NAEP data seemingly support this concern.

Part II
Cracks in
the Foundation?

The Context for Learning Mathematics

Introduction

IN RESPONSE to the wave of information about the poor mathematics achievement of American young people, educators and policymakers have recommended widespread reforms that are setting new cornerstones for mathematics education. For example, the Second International Mathematics Study (SIMS) report calls for fundamental revisions in curriculum, a re-examination of tracking practices, improved textbooks, and increasing the proportions of students in high school mathematics programs.[1] The National Council of Teachers of Mathematics (NCTM) has drafted a set of standards to improve the quality of mathematics curricula (K-12), as well as criteria for evaluating mathematics programs and student achievement. Both the NCTM recommendations and current research on how children learn mathematics emphasize the need for classroom instruction to help students improve their problem solving and reasoning skills. Students may spend far too much time on drill and practice. They need to spend more time investigating the connections among mathematical concepts and to gain more experience solving problems in a rich array of practical situations.

---

[1]Curtis McKnight, et. al., *The Underachieving Curriculum: Assessing U.S. School Mathematics from an International Perspective*. A National Report on the Second International Mathematics Study, International Association for the Evaluation of Education Achievement, Stipes Publishing Company, Champaign, IL, 1987.

Building students' appreciation for the discipline and their self-confidence in doing mathematics is also important to improving mathematics education. Learners must believe in the value of what is being taught and receive encouragement from parents and teachers in order to reach their full potential.

Finally, mathematics educators recommend calculators and computers to help students experience the richness and power of the discipline as they explore realistic problems, complex data sets, and sophisticated graphic displays.

The NAEP mathematics assessments do not provide cause and effect answers, but the results do offer substantial information about indicators of the quality of mathematics education. For example, course enrollment, students' attitudes, laboratory and computer experiences, amount of homework, and instructional materials have been identified as key indicators of the condition of mathematics education.[2] Policymakers and educators can use the NAEP information about patterns and trends in these and other learning contexts as they monitor the success of current reforms.

Overview

Results from the 1986 assessment indicate that while many students enjoy mathematics, most hold negative views on the nature of the discipline and have limited expectations for its relevance to their future lives. Perhaps we should not be surprised at these perceptions, given current approaches to mathematics education. The portrait is one of continuing traditions, in which the prevailing mode of instruction is still that of teachers explaining material and working exercises on the chalkboard. Few students work on projects and laboratory activities, and still fewer collaborate in pairs or small groups. Textbooks and workbooks remain ever present at all grade levels, while other instructional resources such as calculators are used infrequently, particularly by younger students. Computer courses are on the rise, but are not yet commonplace, particularly for students in the lower grades, or for those in the lower range of mathematics performance.

Computer courses are on the rise, but are not yet commonplace . . .

On a more positive note, a rise in the amount of homework and testing in 1986 suggests increased expectations for student performance—perhaps a consequence of states' recent calls for more rigorous academic standards. Yet reform efforts that concentrate only on bolstering homework and testing miss the opportunity for deeper educational changes that seem to be so greatly in need.

---

[2]Richard Murnane and Senta Raizen (Eds.), National Research Council, *Improving Indicators of the Quality of Science and Mathematics Education in Grades K-12*. NRC Committee on Indicators of Precollege Science and Mathematics Education. Washington, DC: National Academy Press, 1988.

The chapters in Part II of this report shed light on some of the curricular and attitudinal factors that appear to have a bearing on students' mathematical proficiency, and consider their implications for educational reform. Chapter 4 reviews current patterns of classroom instruction, with particular attention to teaching practices. Chapter 5 considers the relative uses of various instructional materials, from the traditional textbook to the more recent innovations of the calculator and computer. Chapter 6 presents information on students' attitudes toward and perceptions of mathematics as a discipline. Chapter 7 contemplates the role of home and school expectations in students' learning of the subject. Finally, Chapter 8 reviews the mathematics course-taking patterns of high school students, and considers how well prepared they are for the challenges that will face them in their future work lives.

Analytic Methods Used in Part II

The background questions about school practices, home support, and attitudes were administered to students at the same time and using the same procedures as those for the cognitive questions. Like the cognitive questions, the background questions were administered to systematic samples of students in a way that allowed accurate estimates of responses for the nation as a whole and for subpopulations of interest.

Some of the results are based on responses to individual questions while others are based on the answers to sets of questions. (Please see the Procedural Appendix for a description of methods used to define composite variables across samples of students.)

Throughout the tables presented in Part II, the results for high-school students (both 17-year-olds and eleventh graders) are based on the full sample of respondents, not just those currently enrolled in mathematics classes. (Those not taking a class were asked to answer the background questions based on the last time they studied mathematics.) A comparative analysis revealed few differences in responses between those currently enrolled in mathematics and the entire sample. The results for the entire sample of high school students are essentially the same as the results for those students currently enrolled in mathematics classes.

CHAPTER 4

Are We Teaching Students to Think Mathematically?

Patterns and Trends in Classroom Instruction

SINCE STUDENTS in elementary school learn more mathematics when their teachers allocate more classroom time to the subject, observational data suggesting that students spend much less than one hour a day learning mathematics heightens concern about the quality of that instructional time.[1] Although effective teaching requires the orchestration of a variety of strategies suited to each instructional setting, research in both education and cognitive psychology suggests some changes in how mathematics should be presented to students in the classroom. These include doing more "hands-on" examples with concrete materials and placing more problems in real-world contexts to help students construct useful meanings for mathematical concepts.[2] Because children rarely encounter formal mathematical symbols, terms, and notation outside of the classroom, the early emphasis on practicing computations may

---

[1]David Wiley and Annegret Harnischfeger, "Explosion of a Myth: Quantity of Schooling and Exposure to Instruction, Major Educational Vehicles." *Educational Researcher* 3(4), pp. 7-12, 1974.

[2]Thomas Romberg, "A Common Curriculum for Mathematics." *Individual Differences and the Common Curriculum: Eighty-second Yearbook of the National Society for the Study of Education*. Chicago: University of Chicago Press, p. 124, 1983.

Barbara Vobejda, "A Mathematician's Research on Math Instruction," *Educational Researcher*, 16:9, December 1987.

serve to divorce mathematics from real-world observations.[3] For example, many 5-year-olds who do not know "2 and 2 makes 4" can easily solve simple addition word problems ("If one child is inside a store and two more go in after him, how many children are in the store?").[4]

Once students learn to rely on procedures, they tend to give up on common sense. For example, students may initially learn multiplication by understanding it as a series of repeated additions, but then lose that original meaning after being taught the routine procedures for two- and three-digit multiplication and applying them repeatedly.[5] Students can quote the steps about "crossing out and moving over" as well as recite rules, but they no longer have any idea whether their answers are reasonable. This can lead to preposterous answers and does little to prevent rote implementation of computational procedures based on misconceptions. For example, one child systematically excluded zero from all her computations because "Zero doesn't count for anything," until she was asked to think about her age, which would one day be 10.[6]

Although automaticity of skills is necessary for efficiency, instruction focusing solely on rote practice can erode understanding of fundamental principles and inhibit students' ability to apply routinized mathematics skills to new contexts.

The mathematics assessment asked students to describe their classroom instruction in global ways, including the frequency with which teachers explain mathematics lessons, work problems on the board, ask students to solve problems alone or in small groups, and assign projects and special reports or laboratory activities. (Some comparable information is available from prior assessments, and trends are discussed when possible.)

Although the NAEP data do not provide information about how students are taught specific concepts, the students' responses give some indication of the extent to which teachers are trying out the new kinds of student-centered activities suggested by researchers. If mathematics activities based on conceptual goals, using concrete materials, were being widely incorporated into elementary classrooms goals, third-graders' responses would paint a portrait of relatively varied instruction involving projects and group activities. Instead, students at all three grade levels reported spending considerable time listening to teacher explanations and at the higher grade levels, also watching the teacher work problems on the board. Almost no students at the

---

[3]T. Carpenter and J. M. Moser, "The Acquisition of Addition and Subtraction Concepts in Grades One through Three." *Journal for Research in Mathematics Education* 15, No. 3, 1984.

[4]M. Hughes, *Children and Number: Difficulties in Learning Math*. Oxford: Basil Blackwell, 1986.

[5]Leone Burton, "Mathematical Thinking: The Struggle for Meaning," *Journal for Research in Mathematics Education*, 15:4, January 1984.

[6]H. Ginsburg, *Children's Arithmetic: How They Learn It and How You Teach It*. Austin, TX: Pro-Ed, 1982.

three grade levels reported working problems in small groups or doing reports or laboratory activities; instead, sizable proportions of students reported working problems independently either daily or weekly.

Teacher Explains Mathematics Lessons: Grades 3, 7, and 11

Student reports about the frequency and clarity of teacher explanations are shown in TABLE 4.1 and TABLE 4.2. Even though the amount of teacher explanation overall was relatively consistent across the three grade levels, the difference between upper- and lower-quartile students in the amount of time spent listening to daily teacher explanations increased with each grade level. By grade 11, 83 percent of the upper-quartile students reported listening to daily explanations compared to about two-thirds (65 percent) of the lower-quartile students—a finding that may reflect differences in teaching style associated with ability grouping at the high school level.

| Percentage of Students at Grades 3, 7, and 11 Reporting Frequency of Listening to Teacher Explain Lessons: 1986* | | | | TABLE 4.1 |

How often do you listen to a teacher explain a mathematics lesson?	Daily	Weekly	Less than Weekly	Never
Grade 3	79 (0.9)	16 (0.6)	1 (0.3)	4 (0.6)
Upper Quartile	76 (2.3)	21 (2.0)	1 (0.6)	3 (1.2)
Lower Quartile	78 (1.9)	12 (1.8)	3 (0.7)	7 (1.8)
Grade 7	82 (0.7)	15 (0.7)	2 (0.3)	2 (0.3)
Upper Quartile	87 (2.0)	11 (1.7)	2 (0.8)	1 (0.6)
Lower Quartile	76 (1.7)	19 (1.7)	2 (0.5)	3 (0.6)
Grade 11	74 (1.1)	20 (0.9)	1 (0.3)	5 (0.7)
Upper Quartile	83 (1.6)	16 (1.6)	0 (0.2)	1 (0.3)
Lower Quartile	65 (3.2)	23 (2.6)	2 (0.8)	10 (1.5)

*Jackknifed standard errors are presented in parentheses.

With each successively higher grade level, fewer students reported understanding teachers' explanations, particularly students in the lower quartile. Ninety percent of the third-grade students claimed at least some understanding. However, only about two-thirds of the eleventh graders agreed that they could understand what their teachers were talking about and there was a marked difference between the reports of the higher- and lower-quartile students. Eighty-three percent of the upper-quartile students agreed that they could understand their teachers' explanations versus only 58 percent of the lower-quartile students.

Percentage of Students at Grades 3, 7, and 11 Reporting Understanding Mathematics Class: 1986*

TABLE 4.2

I usually understand what we are talking about in mathematics.

	Percent True	Percent Some
Grade 3	55 (1.0)	36 (1.0)
Upper Quartile	66 (2.6)	30 (2.5)
Lower Quartile	44 (2.1)	37 (2.2)

	Percent Strongly Agree or Agree*
Grade 7	79 (1.5)
Upper Quartile	88 (2.6)
Lower Quartile	70 (3.1)
Grade 11	69 (1.0)
Upper Quartile	83 (2.5)
Lower Quartile	58 (2.8)

*Jackknifed standard errors are presented in parentheses.

Trends in the Role of Teacher Explanations at Age 17

In each of three mathematics assessments from 1978 to 1986, 17-year-old students attending school were asked how frequently their teachers explained mathematics lessons and how often they discussed mathematics in class. As shown in TABLE 4.3, student reports about the use of teacher explanations were remarkably consistent across the eight-year period. In each of the three assessments, approximately 80 percent of the 17-year-olds reported that they "often" listened to explanations of mathematics lessons. In contrast, the use of classroom discussion appears to have increased over time; this may be a positive sign in the context of recent research findings suggesting more student involvement in mathematics classes. About 50 percent of the 17-year-olds in both 1978 and 1982 reported frequent class discussion, compared to 57 percent in 1986.

In contrast, the use of classroom discussion appears to have increased over time . . .

Trends in Percentage of 17-Year-Olds Reporting Frequency of Explanation and Discussion: 1978-1986*			TABLE 4.3

In your high school mathematics courses, how often did you:	Often	Sometimes	Never
Listen to a teacher explain a mathematics lesson?			
1978	79 (1.2)	19 (1.1)	2 (0.4)
1982	77 (1.6)	19 (1.4)	4 (0.4)
1986	81 (1.4)	15 (1.2)	4 (0.6)
Discuss mathematics in class?			
1978	51 (1.5)	43 (1.4)	7 (0.6)
1982	50 (1.7)	42 (1.4)	8 (0.7)
1986	57 (1.4)	35 (1.2)	8 (0.8)

*Jackknifed standard errors are presented in parentheses.

Trend results also suggest changes in the extent to which 17-year-old students reported understanding the material covered in their mathematics classes (TABLE 4.4). More 17-year-olds agreed that they generally understood what was talked about in mathematics in 1986 than in 1978 or 1984, and the increases were uniform across subgroups. It is difficult to know the underlying reasons for such improvements. It is hoped that teachers are presenting mathematics lessons with greater clarity rather than teaching easier material. Also, regardless of reported improvement in this area, about one-fourth of the 17-year-olds in 1986 still reported that they did not usually understand what was talked about in mathematics class.

Trends in Percentages of 17-Year-Olds Reporting Understanding Mathematics Class: 1978-1986*	TABLE 4.4

| | Percent Strongly Agree or Agree | | |
	1978	1982	1986
I usually understand what we are talking about in mathematics.			
Nation	67 (1.4)	69 (1.4)	74 (1.4)
Male	71 (1.7)	72 (2.2)	77 (2.4)
Female	64 (2.0)	66 (1.9)	70 (2.1)
White	67 (1.7)	70 (1.4)	73 (1.8)
Black	72 (3.5)	71 (3.9)	81 (5.6)
Hispanic	62 (5.9)	57 (5.2)	70 (5.3)
Disadvantaged Urban	65 (3.1)	78 (5.1)	86 (6.1)
Advantaged Urban	66 (2.8)	65 (4.4)	73 (5.6)

*Jackknifed standard errors are presented in parentheses.

Board Work by Teachers and Students

As shown in TABLE 4.5, teacher use of the chalkboard also comprises a significant part of mathematics instruction. About three-fourths of the seventh and eleventh graders indicated this was a daily activity, compared to only about one-half of the third graders. Although using the board to illustrate fundamental relationships can be very effective in helping grade-school children understand procedures and concepts, boardwork is probably more appropriately used at the higher grade levels.[7] The differential patterns of board use reported by low- and high-performing students across the grade levels suggest that the role of board work may differ, depending on the complexity of the material being covered. At grade 3, somewhat more lower-quartile students reported watching the teacher work problems on the board than did upper-quartile students. At grade 11, however, 85 percent of the upper-quartile students reported watching their teachers at the board every day, compared to only 58 percent of the lower-quartile students. This may indicate that high-school teachers are using the board for different purposes than elementary teachers, perhaps to explicate more complex information.

---

[7]Magdalene Lampert, "Knowing, Doing, and Teaching Multiplication." *Cognition and Instruction*, Vol. 3(4), 1986.

Although about one-half the students at all three grade levels reported working problems on the board at least weekly, this instructional technique is used somewhat more frequently at the elementary level and with lower-performing students.

Percentage of Students at Grades 3, 7, and 11 Reporting Frequency of Working Mathematics Problems on the Board: 1986*					**TABLE 4.5**

How often do you:	Daily	Weekly	Less than Weekly	Never
Watch the teacher work problems on the board?				
Grade 3	57 (1.3)	33 (1.2)	4 (0.5)	7 (0.6)
Upper Quartile	52 (2.3)	39 (2.6)	4 (1.2)	5 (1.0)
Lower Quartile	55 (2.2)	33 (2.1)	4 (0.7)	8 (1.2)
Grade 7	74 (1.1)	22 (1.1)	2 (0.2)	2 (0.4)
Upper Quartile	79 (2.0)	19 (2.4)	1 (0.4)	1 (0.6)
Lower Quartile	72 (1.4)	22 (1.6)	3 (0.7)	4 (0.7)
Grade 11	73 (1.1)	21 (1.0)	1 (0.3)	5 (0.8)
Upper Quartile	85 (1.9)	14 (1.7)	1 (0.3)	1 (0.6)
Lower Quartile	58 (3.3)	29 (3.3)	3 (0.7)	10 (1.7)
Work mathematics problems at the board?				
Grade 3	15 (1.0)	46 (1.5)	11 (0.9)	27 (1.0)
Upper Quartile	12 (1.5)	50 (3.0)	13 (2.0)	25 (2.3)
Lower Quartile	20 (1.9)	43 (2.4)	10 (1.2)	27 (1.8)
Grade 7	21 (1.2)	32 (1.5)	19 (1.2)	27 (1.7)
Upper Quartile	16 (1.8)	30 (3.3)	19 (2.3)	34 (3.0)
Lower Quartile	28 (2.3)	31 (2.6)	16 (1.9)	25 (2.1)
Grade 11	17 (1.0)	30 (1.3)	14 (1.1)	40 (1.7)
Upper Quartile	13 (2.4)	29 (3.3)	17 (2.3)	41 (3.7)
Lower Quartile	18 (1.6)	30 (2.6)	11 (1.3)	41 (2.4)

*Jackknifed standard errors are presented in parentheses.

Across the three assessments, 17-year-old students indicated that there has been a modest increase in how often teachers use the board accompanied by a modest decrease in how often students themselves are asked to work problems at the board (TABLE 4.6)

Trends in Percentage of 17-Year-Olds Reporting Frequency of Working Mathematics Problems on the Board: 1978-1986*			TABLE 4.6

How often do you:	Often	Sometimes	Never
Watch the teacher work mathematics problems on the board?			
1978	80 (1.1)	18 (0.9)	2 (0.4)
1982	79 (1.5)	19 (1.5)	3 (0.4)
1986	83 (1.0)	14 (0.9)	3 (0.5)
Work mathematics problems at the board?			
1978	28 (1.3)	60 (1.2)	12 (1.0)
1982	26 (1.6)	63 (1.5)	11 (0.9)
1986	26 (1.8)	53 (1.4)	21 (1.6)

*Jackknifed standard errors are presented in parentheses.

Working Problems in Small Groups or Independently

Despite the previously described research recommendations for more "hands-on" mathematics activities, well over half the students at all three grade levels reported that they never work mathematics problems in small groups (TABLE 4.7). However, half the lower-quartile third graders reported working in small groups daily or weekly compared to only about one-third of the upper-quartile students. Consistent with the notion that students spend most of their time in mathematics classes practicing computation, sizable proportions of students at all three grade levels reported working mathematics problems on their own either daily or weekly, with better students being given more independent work than poorer students.

		Table 4.7
Percentage of Students at Grades 3, 7, and 11 Reporting Frequency of Small Group and Independent Work: 1986*		TABLE 4.7

How often do you:	Daily	Weekly	Less than Weekly	Never
Work mathematics problems in small groups?				
Grade 3	12 (0.8)	25 (1.1)	10 (0.9)	53 (1.1)
Upper Quartile	8 (1.2)	23 (2.2)	9 (1.7)	61 (2.0)
Lower Quartile	19 (1.5)	29 (2.1)	14 (1.7)	39 (2.7)
Grade 7	6 (0.5)	11 (0.8)	18 (1.5)	65 (1.7)
Upper Quartile	4 (1.0)	10 (1.6)	19 (2.5)	67 (2.6)
Lower Quartile	10 (1.2)	15 (1.3)	15 (1.9)	61 (1.9)
Grade 11	7 (0.8)	20 (1.5)	14 (1.0)	59 (1.6)
Upper Quartile	8 (1.5)	21 (3.0)	16 (2.4)	55 (2.5)
Lower Quartile	9 (1.9)	19 (2.3)	11 (1.6)	61 (2.6)
Work mathematics problems alone?				
Grade 3	58 (1.1)	30 (1.2)	4 (0.5)	9 (0.7)
Upper Quartile	62 (3.2)	30 (3.2)	1 (0.4)	7 (1.6)
Lower Quartile	54 (1.8)	27 (1.9)	8 (1.4)	11 (1.4)
Grade 7	81 (1.1)	14 (1.0)	2 (0.3)	3 (0.4)
Upper Quartile	87 (1.5)	10 (1.6)	1 (0.6)	1 (0.6)
Lower Quartile	73 (2.2)	17 (1.7)	4 (0.9)	7 (1.0)
Grade 11	71 (1.0)	22 (0.9)	2 (0.4)	5 (0.4)
Upper Quartile	78 (2.0)	20 (2.1)	1 (0.4)	1 (0.5)
Lower Quartile	66 (2.4)	20 (1.7)	3 (1.3)	11 (1.2)

*Jackknifed standard errors are presented in parentheses.

Projects, Reports, and Laboratory Activities

Although one way to help students understand mathematics is by using instructional activities in which students can apply their mathematics skills in real world or laboratory situations, the results indicate students rarely engage in such activities (TABLE 4.8). At both grades 7 and 11, the lower-quartile students indicated doing reports and laboratory activities somewhat more frequently than the top-quartile students, perhaps because such supplemental instruction is used for remediation.

Percentage of Students at Grades 7 and 11 Reporting Frequency of Reports and Laboratory Activities: 1986*				TABLE 4.8

How often do you:	Daily	Weekly	Less than Weekly	Never
Make reports or do projects on mathematics?				
Grade 7	3 (0.4)	5 (0.5)	12 (1.0)	81 (1.3)
Upper Quartile	2 (0.7)	2 (0.6)	13 (2.3)	83 (2.4)
Lower Quartile	6 (0.9)	9 (1.3)	10 (1.4)	75 (2.2)
Grade 11	2 (0.4)	4 (0.6)	7 (0.6)	87 (0.9)
Upper Quartile	1 (0.9)	2 (0.8)	6 (1.2)	91 (1.5)
Lower Quartile	3 (0.9)	5 (1.2)	8 (1.1)	84 (1.6)
Do mathematics laboratory activities?				
Grade 7	4 (0.4)	9 (0.8)	10 (0.8)	78 (1.1)
Upper Quartile	1 (0.4)	5 (1.1)	11 (1.4)	83 (1.6)
Lower Quartile	7 (0.9)	13 (1.3)	7 (1.1)	72 (1.7)
Grade 11	3 (0.5)	7 (0.7)	8 (0.8)	82 (1.1)
Upper Quartile	2 (0.9)	7 (2.3)	10 (2.1)	82 (2.3)
Lower Quartile	4 (0.7)	10 (1.4)	6 (0.9)	80 (1.9)

*Jackknifed standard errors are presented in parentheses.

The trend results for the incidence of students doing reports and projects show little change during the eight-year period from 1978 to 1986 (TABLE 4.9). If anything, the percentage of 17-year-olds who reported never engaging in such activities increased slightly in 1986.

Trends in Percentage of 17-Year-Olds Reporting Frequency of Reports and Projects: 1978-1986*			TABLE 4.9

How often do you: Make reports or do projects on mathematics?	Often	Sometimes	Never
1978	2 (0.2)	23 (1.2)	75 (1.2)
1982	2 (0.3)	22 (1.0)	76 (1.0)
1986	3 (0.5)	18 (1.5)	79 (1.6)

*Jackknifed standard errors are presented in parentheses.

Summary

Instruction in mathematics classes is characterized by teachers explaining material, working problems on the board, and having students work mathematics problems on their own—a characterization that has not changed across the eight-year period from 1978 to 1986.

. . . the rarity of innovative instructional approaches is a matter for true concern.

Considering the prevalence of research suggesting that there may be better ways for students to learn mathematics than by listening to their teachers and then practicing what they have heard in rote fashion, the rarity of innovative instructional approaches is a matter for true concern. Students need to learn to apply their newly acquired mathematics skills by involvement in investigative situations, and their responses indicate very few opportunities to engage in such activities. To improve their understanding of mathematics and their ability to solve mathematical problems, students need the benefit of instruction that emphasizes application of their skills in real-world situations.

CHAPTER 5
Is Technology
the Answer?

Materials for Mathematics Instruction

AS INDICATED in Chapter 4, student reports about what we are doing in our nation's classrooms suggest that routine instructional approaches predominate. An examination of patterns in the teaching materials used—ranging from the traditional workbook and text to the more recently introduced calculator and computer—offers further elaboration of how and what students are learning in mathematics.

. . . routine instructional approaches predominate.

The Prevalence of Textbooks, Workbooks, and Ditto Sheets

The high amount of textbook and workbook usage reported by students in 1986, particularly in grades 7 and 11 (TABLE 5.1), confirms that these materials play a major role in students' understanding of the subject. Forty-one percent of the third graders reported using workbooks on a daily basis, and it is interesting to note that use varied substantially between upper- and lower-quartile students. While upper-quartile students were more likely to report daily or weekly use, twice as many lower-quartile third graders reported never using workbooks—20 percent compared to 9 percent of the upper-quartile students. This may signal that sufficient teaching materials are unavailable in some schools for the lower-performing students, or that teachers do not feel poor-performing students are well enough prepared to use such materials.

The emphasis on instructional materials generally changes from workbooks and ditto sheets to textbooks in junior and senior high schools. Yet, almost one-third (32 percent) of the lower-quartile seventh graders and one-fourth (27 percent) of the lower-quartile eleventh graders reported using workbooks or dittos on a daily basis. This continuing reliance on work sheets for low achieving students was accompanied by less textbook use. For example, 80 percent of the upper-quartile students at grade 11 reported

Percentage of Students at Grades 3, 7, and 11 Reporting Frequency of Using Workbooks and Textbooks: 1986*				TABLE 5.1

How often do you:	Daily	Weekly	Less than Weekly	Never
Use a mathematics workbook or ditto sheets?				
Grade 3	41 (1.4)	40 (1.6)	4 (0.5)	15 (1.4)
Upper Quartile	47 (3.0)	42 (1.9)	3 (0.8)	9 (1.5)
Lower Quartile	36 (2.1)	37 (2.2)	6 (1.0)	20 (2.5)
Grade 7	25 (1.4)	36 (1.4)	18 (1.3)	21 (1.6)
Upper Quartile	18 (2.4)	38 (2.2)	24 (2.3)	20 (2.9)
Lower Quartile	32 (1.9)	55 (1.7)	11 (1.2)	22 (2.2)
Grade 11	16 (1.2)	30 (1.4)	15 (1.2)	38 (1.5)
Upper Quartile	9 (1.4)	26 (1.6)	21 (2.4)	44 (3.4)
Lower Quartile	27 (2.1)	34 (2.0)	9 (1.3)	31 (2.0)
Use a mathematics textbook?				
Grade 7	77 (1.4)	17 (1.0)	3 (0.5)	4 (0.5)
Upper Quartile	84 (2.3)	14 (2.2)	1 (0.6)	1 (0.8)
Lower Quartile	69 (2.1)	18 (1.3)	5 (1.1)	8 (1.1)
Grade 11	76 (1.4)	18 (1.3)	1 (0.2)	5 (0.5)
Upper Quartile	80 (2.6)	18 (2.9)	1 (0.3)	2 (0.5)
Lower Quartile	65 (2.5)	23 (2.3)	2 (0.4)	11 (1.5)

*Because the labels of instructional materials are often used interchangeably in elementary schools, NAEP asked third graders how often they used workbooks or ditto sheets, while seventh and eleventh graders were asked two separate items on how often they used workbooks and textbooks. Jackknifed standard errors are presented in parentheses.

using a textbook every day as compared to only 65 percent of the lower-quartile students. NAEP data suggest that students in the upper quartile of performance at grades 7 and 11 are more likely than those in the lower quartile to use textbooks daily. However, the NAEP data do not address the extent to which use of the textbook is a cause or a byproduct of better performance.

The Uses of Technology

The infiltration of technology into mathematics instruction raises timely questions for research. What are the appropriate roles of calculators and computers in the mathematics classroom? Are these technologies an essential part of the curriculum? What should their relationship be to more traditional classroom resources such as text and workbooks?

To help address these larger questions, NAEP has gathered trend information on students' access to calculators and computers and their reported use of these tools in mathematics classes.

The Availability and Use of Calculators

Most students have calculators available in the home, but relatively few have access to calculators in school (TABLE 5.2). It is disappointing that so few schools, particularly at the elementary level, appear to provide this relatively inexpensive and highly useful technology for students' use in mathematics. The calculator can liberate students from time-consuming computations, freeing them to tackle more challenging tasks.

Most students have calculators available in the home, but relatively few have access to calculators in school . . .

Access to Calculators for Use in Mathematics Class, Grades 3, 7, and 11: 1986*			TABLE 5.2
	Percent "Yes"		
	Grade 3	Grade 7	Grade 11
Do you or your family own a calculator?	82 (0.9)	94 (0.7)	97 (0.7)
Does your school have calculators for use in math class?	15 (1.1)	21 (1.6)	26 (1.9)

*Jackknifed standard errors are presented in parentheses.

Students in the 1986 assessment were asked a series of questions on the extent to which they used calculators both in mathematics class and outside of it, for doing homework, checking problems, or performing routine computations. TABLE 5.3 depicts the percentage of eleventh-grade students in the upper and lower quartiles of performance who reported using the calculator for these and other tasks.

Eleventh graders in the highest quartile of mathematics performance reported using calculators—for homework, checking exercises, doing routine computation, solving problems, and taking tests—considerably more often than did their peers in the lowest quartile of performance. What is most striking is the difference between students who used the calculator for routine computation and those who did not: Students in the upper quartile were nearly twice as likely as those in the lower quartile to use the calculator for routine computation.

Percentage of Grade 11 Students Reporting Uses of Calculators: 1986*		TABLE 5.3

	Percent "Yes"	
	Upper Quartile	Lower Quartile
Do you use calculators:		
a. for homework?	65 (2.9)	39 (2.5)
b. for checking answers?	60 (2.9)	50 (2.3)
c. for routine computation?	49 (3.2)	21 (1.9)
d. for solving problems?	58 (2.5)	43 (2.9)
e. on tests?	49 (3.8)	17 (3.8)

*Jackknifed standard errors are presented in parentheses.

In addition to asking students about their use of the calculator for various tasks, equivalent representative samples of students in each grade level were asked in the 1986 assessment to work a set of common problems, one sample using calculators, and the other not. Their relative performance is exhibited in TABLE 5.4.

Students in grade 3 who used calculators on the set of comparative items averaged almost 20 percent higher than their peers without calculators, while the averages for students in grades 7 and 11 were 13 percent and 8 percent higher, respectively.

<table>
<tr><td>Performance on the Same Items with and without Calculator by Students in Grades 3, 7, and 11: 1986*</td><td>TABLE 5.4</td></tr>
</table>

	Percentage of Items Correct	
	With Calculator	**Without Calculator**
Grade 3 (Based on 11 items)	69 (0.8)*	51 (0.8)
Grade 7 (Based on 30 items)	61 (0.3)*	48 (0.4)
Grade 11 (Based on 32 items)	75 (0.4)*	67 (0.4)

*Statistically significant difference at the .05 level from performance without calculator. Jackknifed standard errors are presented in parentheses.

Despite this evidence of success using calculators in 1986, both the 9-year-olds and the 13-year-olds showed significant declines in their performance using this device across time, while 17-year-olds showed a dip in their performance (TABLE 5.5).

<table>
<tr><td>Trends in Mean Percentages of Success in Using a Calculator for 9-, 13-, and 17-Year-Olds: 1978-1986*</td><td>TABLE 5.5</td></tr>
</table>

	1978	**1982**	**1986**
Age 9 (8 items)	78 (0.9)*	79 (0.8)*	75 (0.7)
Age 13 (8 items)	59 (1.3)*	56 (1.4)	55 (1.4)
Age 17 (11 items)	66 (1.0)	63 (1.0)	65 (1.2)

*Statistically significant difference from 1986 at the .05 level. Jackknifed standard errors are presented in parentheses.

Performance on eight calculator items, mostly whole-number computation, given to 9-year-olds in each of the last three assessments declined significantly from both 1978 and 1982 to 1986.

At age 13, performance also declined significantly on eight items, primarily decimal computation, given across all three assessments. At age 17, performance did not change between 1978 and 1986 on 11 calculator items—both decimal computation and verbal problems—administered in all three assessments.

School mathematics programs have a unique opportunity to instruct students in the use of calculators, and thereby help them to explore a broader range of mathematical concepts and skills. Continued efforts should be made to integrate calculators into the mathematics curriculum so that students can learn the appropriate uses of these tools and realize the efficiencies that they can provide. The fact that students' performance on assessment items requiring calculator use has actually decreased over time suggests that this valuable tool is being neglected in mathematics instruction.

Continued efforts should be made to integrate calculators into the mathematics curriculum . . .

The Availability and Uses of Computers

Findings from the NAEP mathematics assessment can help to inform current discussions concerning the role of the computer in the mathematics curriculum. The results displayed in TABLE 5.6 reveal considerable increases in the percentage of students who report that they have access to computers at school to learn mathematics. Thirteen-year-olds apparently had little access to computers in 1978, but nearly one-half reported access in 1986. At age 17, 24 percent had access in 1978, and this figure more than doubled in 1986 for all groups of students but those in the upper quartile.

Thirteen-year-olds apparently had little access to computers in 1978, but nearly one-half reported access in 1986.

It should be cautioned, however, that much goes under the rubric of computer learning, including everything from computer games, to drill and practice, to more advanced applications. Thus student responses to questions on their use of computers must be viewed with sensitivity to the variety of possible interpretations.

The trends across assessments and across subgroups indicate that access has been relatively equitable. In fact, at age 13, more Black students than White or Hispanic students reported access to computers in the late 1970s and early 1980s. The results for students in the upper- and lower-achievement quartiles suggest, however, that the better mathematics students have more access to computers. Also, more 17-year-olds reported that they had access to computers to learn mathematics than did 13-year-olds. Finally, it is interesting to note that, although 17-year-olds reporting access had higher average proficiency scores, the 13-year-olds showed comparable scores regardless of their access to computers (TABLE 5.7).

. . . although 17-year-olds reporting access had higher average proficiency scores, the 13-year-olds showed comparable scores regardless of their access to computers . . .

TABLE 5.6

Trends in Percentage of Students Reporting Access to Computers for Learning Mathematics at Ages 13 and 17: 1978-1986*

Do you have access to a computer terminal in your school for learning mathematics?

Percent "Yes"

	1978		1982		1986	
	Age 13	Age 17	Age 13	Age 17	Age 13	Age 17
Nation	12 (1.8)	24 (2.6)	23 (2.9)	50 (3.1)	47 (3.0)	57 (2.4)
Male	14 (2.1)	26 (3.3)	23 (3.1)	49 (3.3)	46 (2.9)	58 (2.9)
Female	11 (1.8)	23 (2.6)	23 (3.3)	50 (4.1)	48 (3.7)	56 (2.8)
White	11 (2.0)	25 (2.7)	21 (3.0)	52 (3.2)	48 (3.3)	57 (2.8)
Black	20 (2.8)	21 (3.6)	32 (4.5)	41 (5.4)	45 (3.9)	57 (4.9)
Hispanic	13 (4.5)	18 (4.4)	19 (5.0)	28 (8.6)	42 (8.3)	48 (5.4)
Upper Quartile	11 (2.4)	38 (4.5)	31 (5.3)	66 (4.2)	53 (4.7)	66 (4.0)
Lower Quartile	14 (1.5)	15 (2.3)	18 (2.9)	35 (3.4)	44 (2.9)	48 (3.0)

*Jackknifed standard errors are presented in parentheses.

TABLE 5.7

Trends in Mathematics Proficiency for Students Reporting Access to Computers for Learning Mathematics: 1978-1986*

Do you have access to a computer terminal in your school for learning mathematics?

	1978		1982		1986	
	Yes	No	Yes	No	Yes	No
Age 13	262 (3.9)	270 (1.8)	276 (3.9)	270 (2.2)	272 (2.7)	269 (1.8)
Age 17	314 (2.8)	297 (1.5)	307 (2.0)	292 (2.3)	305 (1.4)	295 (2.0)

*Jackknifed standard errors are presented in parentheses.

As shown in TABLE 5.8, the percentage of students who reported studying mathematics through computerized instruction increased over time, particularly at age 13. In 1986, 39 percent of the 13-year-olds reported computerized mathematics instruction compared to only 22 percent of the

| Trends in Percentage of Students Reporting Computerized Instruction in Mathematics at Ages 13 and 17: 1978-1986* | TABLE 5.8 |

Have you ever studied mathematics through computer instruction?

Percent "Yes"

	1978		1982		1986	
	Age 13	Age 17	Age 13	Age 17	Age 13	Age 17
Nation	14 (0.9)	12 (1.1)	24 (2.3)	19 (1.5)	39 (2.4)	22 (1.5)
Male	16 (1.4)	14 (1.9)	25 (2.3)	22 (2.0)	41 (2.2)	24 (1.9)
Female	13 (0.9)	11 (1.3)	22 (2.5)	16 (1.6)	37 (3.3)	20 (2.4)
White	14 (1.2)	12 (1.2)	22 (2.0)	17 (1.5)	39 (2.7)	22 (1.5)
Black	19 (2.8)	17 (4.6)	36 (5.9)	25 (3.2)	37 (3.7)	25 (3.9)
Hispanic	9 (4.3)	8 (2.8)	20 (5.2)	27 (5.3)	41 (11.6)	20 (4.8)
Upper Quartile	16 (1.9)	19 (3.5)	28 (2.7)	24 (2.6)	46 (3.2)	29 (3.2)
Lower Quartile	15 (1.5)	11 (1.3)	20 (3.0)	15 (2.9)	35 (4.2)	21 (1.8)

Average Mathematics Proficiency for Students Reporting Computerized Instruction in Mathematics

	1978		1982		1986	
	Yes	No	Yes	No	Yes	No
Age 13	267 (3.2)	267 (1.6)	276 (2.0)	269 (2.0)	273 (2.5)	267 (2.5)
Age 17	309 (4.4)	299 (1.4)	303 (2.7)	299 (2.3)	304 (2.0)	301 (1.3)

*Jackknifed standard errors are presented in parentheses.

17-year-olds; thus, studying some aspects of mathematics through computerized instruction seems to be more prevalent in the middle-school years.

In 1986, about one-half to two-thirds of the 13- and 17-year-olds reported they had used a computer to solve a mathematics problem (TABLE 5.9). At

84

age 13, this type of use peaked for most subpopulations in 1982. Only males and students in the top quartile reported increased use from 1982 to 1986. At age 17, more students reported using computers to solve problems in 1982 than in 1978, but the percentages leveled off in 1986. Students who reported

Trends in Percentage of 13- and 17-Year-Olds Reporting Using Computers for Problem Solving in Mathematics*

TABLE 5.9

Have you ever used a computer to solve a mathematical problem?

Percent "Yes"

	1978		1982		1986	
	Age 13	Age 17	Age 13	Age 17	Age 13	Age 17
Nation	56 (1.4)	46 (1.5)	66 (1.7)	51 (1.8)	64 (2.2)	52 (1.8)
Male	58 (1.8)	51 (2.4)	64 (2.4)	59 (1.9)	69 (1.9)	60 (2.3)
Female	55 (1.9)	42 (1.7)	69 (2.0)	44 (2.4)	59 (3.3)	46 (1.9)
White	57 (1.5)	48 (1.6)	66 (1.9)	51 (1.9)	66 (2.3)	52 (2.0)
Black	51 (4.2)	38 (3.6)	71 (4.5)	52 (3.7)	65 (3.9)	55 (3.7)
Hispanic	54 (7.6)	41 (5.1)	63 (5.6)	53 (9.6)	53 (7.3)	50 (4.8)
Upper Quartile	59 (2.5)	54 (3.3)	71 (2.7)	56 (2.3)	76 (2.3)	62 (2.9)
Lower Quartile	54 (2.6)	44 (2.5)	61 (3.3)	51 (3.8)	57 (3.8)	46 (3.1)

Average Mathematics Proficiency for Students Reporting Using Computers for Problem Solving

	1978		1982		1986	
	Yes	No	Yes	No	Yes	No
Age 13	268 (1.8)	264 (2.0)	272 (1.8)	268 (2.9)	273 (2.0)	264 (2.8)
Age 17	303 (2.1)	297 (1.8)	300 (1.8)	299 (2.7)	305 (1.4)	298 (1.4)

*Jackknifed standard errors are presented in parentheses.

that they had used a computer for problem solving tended to have higher mathematics proficiency levels than those who had not.

The percentage of students exposed to computer programming courses also increased greatly across the 1978, 1982, and 1986 assessments, reflecting the growth of instruction in computer programming in the secondary school curriculum (TABLE 5.10). This pattern of increased computer coursework was consistent for all demographic subpopulations across the recent assessments. The data do show that the enrollment in these courses started, and has remained, much greater for male than female students. However, the percentages of White, Black, and Hispanic students enrolled in computer programming classes are roughly equal within each of the assessments.

Trends in Percentages of 17-Year-Olds Who Have Taken Coursework in Computer Programming: 1978-1986*			TABLE 5.10

| | Percent "Yes" | | |
	1978	1982	1986
In school, have you taken a course in computer programming?			
Nation	10 (0.9)	15 (0.9)	32 (1.1)
Male	12 (1.2)	16 (1.0)	36 (1.6)
Female	9 (0.9)	13 (0.8)	28 (1.2)
White	10 (1.0)	15 (1.0)	32 (1.2)
Black	9 (0.9)	16 (1.6)	30 (3.5)
Hispanic	7 (1.5)	12 (1.8)	29 (3.0)

*Jackknifed standard errors are presented in parentheses.

TABLE 5.11 presents the average proficiency scores for 17-year-old students relative to their coursework in computer programming for each of the last three mathematics assessments. The results show that students who have taken coursework in computer programming exhibit consistently higher proficiency scores than those who have not. Nevertheless, the trend for these more able students over the three assessments shows a significant decline in mathematics achievement since 1978. In comparison, students who have not studied computer programming only experienced a dip in 1982 and a return to original proficiency levels in 1986.

At a glance, the downward trend in proficiency scores among students who have taken a course in computer programming seems to contradict expectations. One might expect programming experience to raise average profi-

Trends in Mathematics Proficiency for 17-Year-Olds by Computer Programming Coursework: 1978-1986	TABLE 5.11

In school, have you taken a course in computer programming?

	1978	1982	1986
Yes	318 (1.8)*	310 (1.2)	312 (1.4)
No	300 (0.8)	297 (1.0)*	301 (0.8)

*Statistically significant difference from 1986 at the .05 level.
 Jackknifed standard errors are presented in parentheses.

ciency. However, as demonstrated in TABLE 5.12, it is the students in lower-level mathematics courses who comprise the greatest increase in computer programming course enrollment from 1978 to 1986—not students in more advanced courses, whose enrollment in programming courses has risen relatively little. Over the same period of time, average proficiency for those who have taken a course in computer programming has decreased

Trends in Percentages of 17-Year-Olds with Computer Programming Coursework by Highest Level of Mathematics Course Taken: 1978-1986*	TABLE 5.12

In school, have you taken a course in computer programming?

	Percent "Yes"		
	1978	1982	1986
Highest Level of Mathematics Course Taken			
Pre-algebra (or less advanced)	4 (3.1)	6 (2.9)	20 (1.9)
Algebra I (first year)	5 (2.8)	9 (2.4)	25 (1.6)
Geometry	8 (2.6)	11 (2.3)	26 (1.6)
Algebra II (second year)	13 (2.2)	19 (1.8)	39 (1.0)
Pre-calculus or Calculus	40 (1.0)	46 (0.8)	49 (0.7)

*Jackknifed standard errors are presented in parentheses.

significantly. The expectation that computer programming would somehow equalize the mathematics performance of less and more able students has clearly not been borne out. While the proficiency of less advanced students may have increased as a result of their programming experience, it has obviously not matched that of their more advanced peers. Instead, as the proportion of less advanced students with programming coursework has increased, average proficiency for *all* students with experience in computer programming has declined.

. . . average proficiency for all students with experience in computer pro- gramming has declined.

NAEP also asked 13- and 17-year-olds if they had ever written a computer program to solve a mathematics problem. The results across assessments are shown in TABLE 5.13. The percentage of 17-year-olds reporting they had written programs compares to the percentage reporting programming coursework. Those reporting such experiences tended to have higher proficiency levels. The patterns for the 13-year-olds differed from those reported by the high-school students. As with the other computer and mathematics learning questions, the percentage of 13-year-olds who reported having written programs to solve problems tended to peak for a number of subgroups in 1982, including students in the lowest quartile. In both 1978 and 1982, proficiency levels were lower for 13-year-olds who reported creating computer programs. In combination, these findings suggest that such activities were initially used more frequently with the poorer students, a practice that seems to have changed in recent years. In 1986, more 13-year-olds in the top quartile reported writing programs to solve mathematics problems.

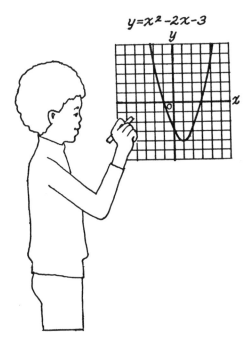

<table>
<tr><td>

Trends in Percentage of 13- and 17-Year-Olds Reporting Writing Computer Programs to Solve Mathematics Problems: 1978-1986*

</td><td>TABLE 5.13</td></tr>
</table>

Have you ever written
a computer program to solve
a mathematical problem?

Percent "Yes"

	1978		1982		1986	
	Age 13	Age 17	Age 13	Age 17	Age 13	Age 17
Nation	29 (1.1)	18 (1.4)	40 (1.5)	24 (1.3)	43 (2.2)	34 (1.7)
Male	31 (1.6)	22 (2.4)	41 (2.0)	29 (2.2)	50 (3.0)	42 (2.5)
Female	27 (1.5)	14 (1.6)	39 (2.0)	20 (1.6)	37 (2.8)	26 (1.9)
White	26 (1.3)	18 (1.5)	38 (1.7)	23 (1.4)	43 (2.6)	33 (1.9)
Black	40 (4.7)	25 (3.2)	52 (4.1)	31 (2.2)	47 (3.4)	38 (3.7)
Hispanic	41 (2.8)	8 (3.1)	47 (4.3)	28 (8.4)	42 (7.7)	39 (5.4)
Upper Quartile	26 (1.9)	27 (4.0)	35 (3.5)	30 (2.7)	52 (3.2)	48 (3.8)
Lower Quartile	35 (2.3)	17 (1.6)	46 (2.3)	24 (1.9)	45 (4.0)	30 (2.6)

Average Mathematics Proficiency for Students Reporting Writing
Computer Programs to Solve Mathematics Problems

	1978		1982		1986	
	Yes	No	Yes	No	Yes	No
Age 13	267 (3.2)	267 (1.6)	266 (2.4)	274 (2.2)	271 (2.1)	269 (2.8)
Age 17	307 (4.0)	299 (1.4)	302 (3.1)	299 (1.9)	307 (2.1)	299 (1.2)

*Jackknifed standard errors are presented in parentheses.

Students' Attitudes Toward Computers

In addition to inquiring about students' access to computer technology and their experiences in using computers to learn mathematics, the 1986 assessment included a battery of questions that measured students' attitudes about computer usage and experience. Responses were grouped according to their overall attitude, and FIGURE 5.1 shows the relationship between these computer attitudes (high, medium, low) and students' performance on the mathematics assessment scale.

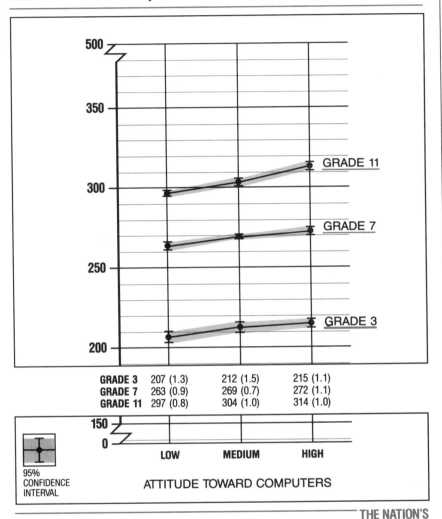

	LOW	MEDIUM	HIGH
GRADE 3	207 (1.3)	212 (1.5)	215 (1.1)
GRADE 7	263 (0.9)	269 (0.7)	272 (1.1)
GRADE 11	297 (0.8)	304 (1.0)	314 (1.0)

ATTITUDE TOWARD COMPUTERS

95% CONFIDENCE INTERVAL

THE NATION'S REPORT CARD

* Jackknifed standard errors are presented in parentheses.

An examination of FIGURE 5.1 reveals a positive relationship between positive attitudes about computer technology and its use in the teaching and learning of mathematics, and higher performance on the mathematics scale.

All of the information derived from the analysis of the NAEP questions relating to computers and mathematics instruction indicates increased activity involving computers in the classroom. Parts of the information suggest that these influences are positive, but others raise questions for educators about the extent to which this kind of instruction can help improve math performance. Lack of evidence on the effects of computer use on mathematics proficiency can be expected in that we are just in the infancy of learning how best to use the computer to assist student learning. With the exception of programming classes *per se,* or the drill and practice used in some classes, relatively few students have had consistent use of computers integrated into their learning of mathematics. Further, the proficiency differences reported may reflect changes in the populations of students using computers rather than the impact of computer use itself.

Summary

Despite the advent of new technologies, there appears to have been little movement in the mathematics curriculum away from the past reliance on teacher and textbook. The calculator holds great promise in helping students to compute, yet its availability and usage in mathematics classrooms is surprisingly limited. And while computers have become a more dominant presence in schools, particularly at the upper grades, most of their use tends to be limited to students at the higher range of mathematical ability and has not trickled down into the lower levels of curriculum.

As asserted by the National Research Council, the rise of the personal computer makes this a particularly opportune time to rethink the mathematics curriculum, and technology's role within it. Not only does the computer introduce an entirely new subject area, but it also creates opportunities for revitalizing traditional subject matter and instructional methods.[1] The results of the 1986 NAEP mathematics assessment indicate that we have far to go before our nation's schools fully exploit the growing availability of technological resources.

... the rise of the personal computer makes this a particularly opportune time to rethink the mathematics curriculum, and technology's role within it.

---

[1]Richard Murnane and Senta Raizen (Eds.), National Research Council, *Improving Indicators of the Quality of Science and Mathematics Education in Grades K-12.* NRC Committee on Indicators of Precollege Science and Mathematics Education. Washington, DC: National Academy Press, 1988.

CHAPTER 6
Does Mathematics Count Beyond School?

Students' Perceptions of Mathematics

I N ITS preliminary version of the new Curriculum and Evaluation Standards, released in 1987, the National Council of Teachers of Mathematics (NCTM) recommended that learning mathematics should require students not only to master essential skills and concepts, but also to develop confidence in their mathematical abilities, and to value mathematics as a discipline.[1]

As set forth in the statement of objectives for the 1986 NAEP mathematics assessment, students responded to a number of questions designed to elicit their perceptions of mathematics.[2] These included questions about:

■ personal experience with mathematics, including students' enjoyment of the subject and level of confidence in their mathematical abilities;

■ value of mathematics, including students' perceptions of its present utility and its expected relevance to future work and life requirements;

■ the nature of mathematics, including students' identification of the salient features of the discipline.

Although only limited information is available on trends in students' attitudes and beliefs about mathematics and on the relationship between these changes and trends in proficiency, results are presented below whenever relevant.

---

[1] *Curriculum and Evaluation Standards for School Mathematics.* National Council of Teachers of Mathematics, Inc., Working Draft, Reston, VA, 1987.

[2] *Math Objectives, 1985-86 Assessment*, National Assessment of Educational Progress, Educational Testing Service, Princeton, NJ, 1985.

Students' Personal Experience with Mathematics

In 1986, all questions measuring students' perceptions of mathematics—including items on beliefs, values, and attitudes—were compiled in a general background indicator for comparison with mathematics proficiency scores. The results of this analysis are displayed in FIGURE 6.1, which plots the average mathematical proficiency scores for students in grades 3, 7, and 11

Average Mathematics Proficiency by Students' Perceptions of Mathematics Grades 3, 7, and 11: 1986* FIGURE 6.1

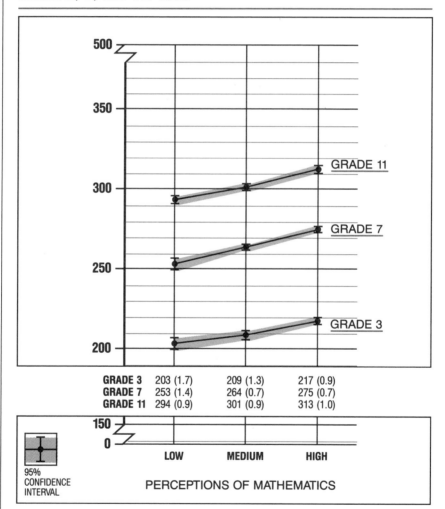

	LOW	MEDIUM	HIGH
GRADE 3	203 (1.7)	209 (1.3)	217 (0.9)
GRADE 7	253 (1.4)	264 (0.7)	275 (0.7)
GRADE 11	294 (0.9)	301 (0.9)	313 (1.0)

95% CONFIDENCE INTERVAL

PERCEPTIONS OF MATHEMATICS

---

* Jackknifed standard errors are presented in parentheses.

against the three dispositional levels—low, medium, and high—that comprise the background indicator.

As depicted, a positive relationship exists at all three grade levels between students' perceptions of mathematics and their proficiency in the subject. Those who enjoy mathematics, perceive its value as a discipline, and appreciate its relevance to daily life are also likely to exhibit somewhat higher levels of mathematical proficiency.

Although the data do not permit NAEP to ascertain which comes first, students' affirmative perceptions of mathematics or their greater proficiency, researchers have posited that attitudes developed early in schooling can play a critical role in fostering continued interest and subsequent coursework in mathematics.[3]

Personal Experience with Mathematics Across the Grades

In 1986, students in grade 3 were asked three questions designed to collect information on their enjoyment of and confidence in mathematics. Responses to these questions are summarized in TABLE 6.1.

Although nearly two-thirds (65 percent) of the students in grade 3 reported that they were good with numbers, and 60 percent stated that they enjoyed the subject, only 40 percent wanted to work at a job using mathematics. These results were fairly consistent across gender and racial/ethnic groups. In summary, while most elementary school students appeared to be relatively confident of their mathematical abilities, even at this early age less than half wanted mathematics to be a part of their future work lives.

[3]Sheila Tobias, *Succeed with Math: Every Student's Guide to Conquering Mathematics Anxiety*. The College Entrance Examination Board, New York, 1987.

Personal Experience with Mathematics, Grade 3: 1986*	TABLE 6.1

Enjoyment	Percent True
I like mathematics.	
Nation	60 (1.5)
Male	60 (1.7)
Female	60 (2.4)
White	58 (1.4)
Black	61 (3.3)
Hispanic	70 (3.2)
I would like to work at a job using mathematics.	
Nation	40 (1.3)
Male	43 (1.6)
Female	38 (2.1)
White	38 (1.6)
Black	48 (2.6)
Hispanic	43 (2.3)
Confidence	
I am good with numbers.	
Nation	65 (1.2)
Male	66 (1.7)
Female	64 (1.8)
White	65 (1.4)
Black	66 (3.2)
Hispanic	65 (3.4)

*Jackknifed standard errors are presented in parentheses.

By grade 11, the percentage of students who stated that they enjoyed mathematics or were good at it declined to approximately one-half.

Similar questions on enjoyment of and confidence in mathematics were asked of students in grades 7 and 11, and their responses are displayed in TABLE 6.2. Minor differences in the phrasing of questions notwithstanding, students in grade 7 appeared to view mathematics slightly less positively than their grade 3 counterparts. Slightly more than half (55 percent) of the seventh-grade students reported that they enjoyed mathematics, and 60 percent believed that they were good at it.

By grade 11, the percentage of students who stated that they enjoyed mathematics or were good at it declined to approximately one-half. In

<table>
<tr><td></td><td colspan="2">Personal Experience of Mathematics
Grades 7 and 11: 1986*</td><td>TABLE 6.2</td></tr>
</table>

Enjoyment	Percent Strongly Agree or Agree	
	Grade 7	Grade 11

I enjoy mathematics.

	Grade 7	Grade 11
Nation	55 (1.5)	50 (1.5)
Male	54 (2.2)	51 (1.9)
Female	57 (2.1)	49 (2.2)
White	54 (1.7)	47 (1.8)
Black	63 (3.2)	62 (3.2)
Hispanic	53 (4.2)	56 (6.1)

I feel good when I solve a mathematics problem by myself.

	Grade 7	Grade 11
Nation	84 (1.6)	88 (1.9)
Male	80 (1.7)	86 (2.8)
Female	89 (2.3)	91 (3.0)
White	84 (1.9)	87 (1.8)
Black	90 (3.0)	94 (4.5)
Hispanic	81 (3.6)	89 (5.8)

Confidence

I am good at mathematics.

	Grade 7	Grade 11
Nation	60 (1.6)	53 (1.7)
Male	64 (2.1)	58 (2.5)
Female	57 (2.3)	48 (1.9)
White	62 (2.0)	53 (1.9)
Black	58 (3.0)	55 (2.9)
Hispanic	50 (4.9)	46 (4.4)

	Percent Very Easy or Easy	
	Grade 7	Grade 11

How easy or hard is mathematics?

	Grade 7	Grade 11
Nation	51 (1.3)	40 (1.5)
Male	51 (2.0)	42 (1.9)
Female	51 (2.0)	38 (2.1)
White	50 (1.5)	39 (1.7)
Black	60 (3.5)	44 (3.0)
Hispanic	51 (2.8)	41 (4.1)

*Jackknifed standard errors are presented in parentheses.

addition, eleventh graders were more likely to perceive mathematics as difficult than were seventh graders. Whereas 51 percent of the seventh graders felt that mathematics was easy, only 40 percent of the eleventh graders held this view. In summary, students' enjoyment of and confidence in mathematics appeared to wane as they proceeded through school, and this pattern was relatively uniform for males and females, as well as for White, Black, and Hispanic students.

Trends in Personal Experience with Mathematics

Using students' stated wishes to take more mathematics courses as an indication of their enjoyment of the subject, it appeared that fewer 13-year-olds were enjoying mathematics in 1986 than in previous assessments in 1978 and 1982. However, as depicted in TABLE 6.3, 17-year-olds showed relatively consistent levels of enjoyment over time.

From 1978 to 1982, confidence in their own mathematical ability appeared to increase significantly for both 13- and 17-year-olds; however, the trend leveled off from 1982 to 1986. These patterns over time were generally consistent for males and females, with the exception of 17-year-old females, whose reported confidence in mathematics steadily increased from 1978 to 1986.

These results do not readily correspond to the trends in average proficiency described in Chapter 1. Thirteen-year-olds' performance improved significantly from 1978 to 1982; during this time they reported decreased enjoyment of mathematics but increased confidence. However, 17-year-olds' performance improved significantly from 1982 to 1986, and during this time period, they reported little change in their enjoyment of mathematics, and only a moderate increase in their confidence in the subject.

There is some concern among educators that society tends to perceive males as more mathematically inclined than females . . .

Although the percentage of females who believe that they are good in mathematics rose over the last three assessments, it must still be noted that the trends for females in both age groups have remained from 7 to 11 percentage points below those for males. There is some concern among educators that society tends to perceive males as more mathematically inclined than females and that this prevalent view has a negative effect on females' ambitions and confidence in the subject. To address this concern, recent NAEP assessments have included a question designed to measure the incidence of sex-role stereotyping among 13- and 17-year-olds.

97

Enjoyment	Percent Strongly Agree or Agree		
	1978	1982	1986
I would like to take more mathematics.			
Nation: 13	50 (1.6)	47 (1.7)	43 (2.6)
17	39 (1.9)	41 (1.6)	38 (1.6)
Male: 13	50 (2.1)	46 (2.9)	46 (3.7)
17	42 (2.5)	43 (1.9)	40 (2.1)
Female: 13	49 (2.3)	48 (2.6)	40 (2.3)
17	36 (2.1)	39 (2.1)	36 (2.1)
Confidence			
I am good at mathematics.			
Nation: 13	65 (1.5)	71 (1.8)	71 (1.7)
17	54 (1.7)	58 (1.6)	61 (1.6)
Male: 13	70 (2.1)	76 (2.8)	74 (2.3)
17	59 (2.2)	63 (2.1)	66 (2.0)
Female: 13	59 (2.0)	66 (1.8)	67 (2.3)
17	49 (2.1)	53 (2.1)	55 (2.1)

*Jackknifed standard errors are presented in parentheses.

As indicated in TABLE 6.4, only a small percentage of students in each age group hold the view that mathematics is "more for boys than girls." However, in 1986, significantly more 13-year-old females agreed with this statement than in either 1978 or 1982. The overall response pattern for males and females at ages 13 and 17 indicates slight movement toward increased sex-role stereotyping.

Although they have not been matched to date by declines in females' mathematical performance, recent findings that a lower percentage of females than males believe that they are good in mathematics, together with a slight increase in sex-role stereotyping, may be cause for concern and attention.

Trends for 13- and 17-Year-Olds Mathematics and Sex-Role Stereotyping: 1978-1986*			TABLE 6.4

	Percent Strongly Agree or Agree*		
Mathematics is more for boys than girls.	1978	1982	1986
Nation: 13	2.5 (0.3)	3.3 (0.5)	6.1 (0.8)
17	2.2 (0.4)	2.4 (0.4)	3.1 (0.6)
Male: 13	3.4 (0.6)	4.3 (0.6)	6.2 (1.0)
17	3.0 (0.7)	3.3 (0.6)	4.2 (1.0)
Female: 13	1.7 (0.3)	2.3 (0.7)	6.1 (0.9)
17	1.5 (0.4)	1.5 (0.4)	2.0 (0.6)

*Jackknifed standard errors are presented in parentheses.

Students' Perceptions of the Value and Utility of Mathematics

Students in grades 7 and 11 were asked a number of questions to determine if they believed mathematics to be useful in solving everyday problems, or would be applicable in their future careers. Results for several of these questions are presented in TABLE 6.5.

Approximately three-fourths of the seventh and eleventh graders reported that mathematics has practical use and is applicable in solving everyday problems. This recognition of the general utility of mathematical skills prevailed across gender and racial/ethnic groups.

. . . it is unfortunate that a majority of the high school students did not see mathematical skills and understanding as any part of their future work.

Although most students appeared to recognize some practical value for the subject area, less than half at either grade level expected to work some day in an area requiring mathematics. While slightly more males and Black students anticipated using mathematics in their future jobs, it is unfortunate that a majority of the high school students did not see mathematical skills and understanding as any part of their future work.

The finding is especially troublesome given the extent to which mathematical tasks permeate virtually all sectors of the labor market. Although few occupations require extensive use of sophisticated mathematics, virtually all involve responsibilities that rely on a mastery of basic quantitative concepts and procedures—such as estimating costs, scheduling tasks, and calculating

	Value of Mathematics, Grades 7 and 11: 1986*		TABLE 6.5

	Percent Strongly Agree or Agree	
	Grade 7	Grade 11
Most of mathematics has practical use.		
Nation	80 (1.3)	81 (1.9)
Male	79 (1.7)	82 (2.9)
Female	81 (1.8)	80 (2.3)
White	81 (1.7)	80 (1.9)
Black	78 (2.6)	85 (3.8)
Hispanic	75 (3.6)	82 (5.0)
Mathematics is useful in solving everyday problems.		
Nation	74 (1.3)	72 (1.5)
Male	73 (1.9)	73 (2.3)
Female	76 (2.1)	71 (2.0)
White	76 (1.8)	71 (1.8)
Black	69 (3.3)	81 (4.0)
Hispanic	68 (3.8)	72 (5.5)
Mathematics helps a person to think logically.		
Nation	64 (1.6)	71 (1.9)
Male	64 (2.4)	72 (2.8)
Female	65 (1.9)	70 (2.1)
White	64 (2.1)	71 (2.3)
Black	67 (4.3)	73 (3.3)
Hispanic	61 (3.1)	65 (5.1)

When you think about what you will do when you are older, do you expect that you will work in an area that requires mathematics?

	Percent Yes	
	Grade 7	Grade 11
Nation	44 (0.9)	47 (1.1)
Male	48 (1.3)	53 (1.5)
Female	40 (1.3)	40 (1.7)
White	46 (1.3)	45 (1.3)
Black	39 (2.7)	51 (2.8)
Hispanic	37 (3.2)	48 (3.8)

*Jackknifed standard errors are presented in parentheses.

budgets. That half of the students in grades 7 and 11 did not expect to work in an area requiring mathematical skills suggests a disaffiliation in students' minds between mathematics as it is taught and mathematics as it is applied in everyday work and life settings.

Mathematics as a Discipline

In addition to asking students about their self-confidence in mathematics and their perceptions of its utilitarian value, the 1986 assessment included questions on the nature of the discipline itself. Do students view mathematics as a dynamic subject, open to discoveries and innovations, or do they perceive it as static and immutable? Do students believe that mathematics is a cohesive body of related subdisciplines—such as algebra, geometry, and calculus—or do they believe that these are disparate subjects, whose particular rules must be committed to memory? Responses for seventh- and eleventh-grade students are presented in TABLE 6.6.

In general, perceptions of the discipline were quite similar for students in grades 7 and 11. Nearly one-half of the students at both grade levels agreed that mathematics is mostly memorizing. Although these perceptions were remarkably similar across demographic subgroups, analysis by quartiles yielded several interesting findings. As may be expected, students in the lower quartile of mathematical performance had a bleaker picture of the dynamic nature of mathematics than those in the upper quartile, possibly because these less able students had not been given the opportunity to see mathematics as a subject in which they can become involved. In fact, almost 60 percent of the eleventh graders in the lower quartile reported that mathematics is mostly memorizing, while only 34 percent of the upper-quartile students viewed mathematics in this manner.

More than 80 percent of both the seventh- and eleventh-graders viewed mathematics as a rule-bound subject—that is, a discipline in which there is always a rule to follow. A commensurate proportion, however, also reported that knowing why an answer is correct is as important as knowing how to find the answer.

Since most seventh and eleventh graders also believe that mathematics helps a person to think logically (TABLE 6.5), these findings seemingly pose a contradiction. Students may see the need to understand mathematics, yet judging from their responses to questions on the roles of memorization and rule application, they may simply feel that it is important to memorize which rule will lead them to the correct answer. Thus the logical value of mathematics that they affirm may be the logic of applying rules, and not of understanding the reasoning that underlies these applications.

TABLE 6.6

Mathematics as a Discipline, Grades 7 and 11: 1986*

	Percent Strongly Agree or Agree	
	Grade 7	Grade 11
Learning mathematics is mostly memorizing.		
Nation	50 (1.4)	48 (1.3)
Upper Quartile	44 (2.0)	33 (2.5)
Lower Quartile	56 (2.2)	61 (2.3)
There is always a rule to follow in mathematics.		
Nation	83 (1.4)	81 (1.5)
Upper Quartile	84 (3.2)	76 (3.4)
Lower Quartile	79 (3.6)	84 (3.0)
Mathematicians work with symbols rather than ideas.		
Nation	36 (0.9)	36 (1.3)
Upper Quartile	32 (2.1)	25 (2.2)
Lower Quartile	42 (2.0)	44 (2.9)
Mathematics is made up of unrelated topics.		
Nation	23 (1.0)	19 (0.9)
Upper Quartile	8 (1.6)	8 (1.6)
Lower Quartile	33 (2.1)	31 (2.0)
New discoveries are seldom made in mathematics.		
Nation	33 (1.3)	24 (1.3)
Upper Quartile	23 (2.2)	18 (2.0)
Lower Quartile	40 (2.4)	31 (3.2)
Knowing why an answer is correct is as important as getting the correct answer.		
Nation	82 (2.1)	89 (1.6)
Upper Quartile	91 (3.7)	92 (4.2)
Lower Quartile	74 (3.3)	85 (3.5)

*Jackknifed standard errors are presented in parentheses.

The mathematics curriculum has been criticized by some educators for its fragmentation, as relationships among various subdisciplines are seldom taught. However, most students in the NAEP assessment did not claim to see mathematics as composed of unrelated topics. It may be that students are referring to the relationships between subskills—such as adding fractions with like denominators—rather than between geometry and measurement, or even addition and multiplication. The strong curricular emphasis on subskill development would support this plausible interpretation.

In summary, students reported mixed perceptions of mathematics as a discipline. While few agreed that discoveries are seldom made in mathematics, most perceived the subject as rule-bound.

Trends in Perceptions of Mathematics as a Discipline

Two questions on the nature of mathematics as a discipline were included in the 1978, 1982, and 1986 mathematics assessments of 13- and 17-year-olds (TABLE 6.7). For males and females in both age groups, smaller proportions of students in 1986 than in 1978 agreed that mathematics helps a person to think logically.

Over the three assessments, an increasing percentage of 17-year-olds agreed with the statement that new discoveries are seldom made in mathematics. While 19 percent held this view in 1978, the proportion rose to 35 percent in 1986. In both 1978 and 1986, 36 to 38 percent of the 13-year-olds agreed with this restrictive view of the discipline of mathematics.

As with the trends for attitudinal questions discussed earlier, responses to questions on the nature of mathematics as a dynamic discipline show little apparent relationship to trends in levels of mathematics proficiency. Given that improvements in student performance occurred predominantly on lower-level items, however, one might not expect an increased appreciation of the potential for innovation in mathematics.

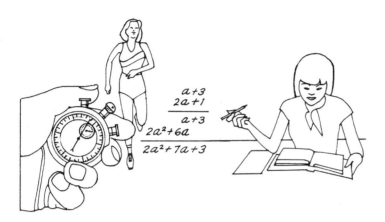

$$\frac{\begin{array}{c} a+3 \\ 2a+1 \end{array}}{\begin{array}{c} a+3 \\ 2a^2+6a \end{array}}$$
$$2a^2+7a+3$$

Trends for 13- and 17-Year-Olds' Views of Mathematics as a Discipline: 1978-1986*			TABLE 6.7

	Percent Strongly Agree or Agree		
	1978	**1982**	**1986**
Mathematics helps a person to think logically.			
Nation: 13	74 (1.6)	75 (2.1)	67 (1.5)
17	77 (1.8)	79 (2.1)	73 (1.7)
Male: 13	76 (2.5)	74 (3.0)	71 (2.2)
17	78 (2.3)	79 (3.1)	76 (2.3)
Female: 13	72 (2.0)	76 (2.8)	63 (2.5)
17	75 (2.3)	79 (2.5)	70 (2.4)
New discoveries are seldom made in mathematics.			
Nation: 13	36 (1.4)	31 (1.3)	38 (1.4)
17	19 (1.4)	23 (1.1)	35 (4.3)
Male: 13	36 (1.7)	32 (1.9)	41 (2.2)
17	19 (2.1)	23 (1.4)	39 (2.0)
Female: 13	35 (2.2)	29 (1.9)	35 (1.7)
17	18 (1.7)	23 (1.9)	30 (1.4)

*Jackknifed standard errors are presented in parentheses.

Summary

Students' general disposition toward mathematics is positively related to their proficiency in the subject. However, changes in attitudes and beliefs from assessment to assessment do not appear to be directly related to trends in mathematics proficiency levels.

Students appear to have more confidence in their mathematical abilities than affinity for the discipline, but both confidence and enjoyment seem to decline as they progress through school. Although students' confidence increased from 1978 to 1986, this was generally not true for their enjoyment of the subject. Most students seem to understand the utility of mathematics in everyday life, but less than half envision that they will have a job that requires their using mathematics. Finally, students perceive mathematics primarily as rule-bound, and their perceptions of the dynamism of the subject have not improved from 1978 to 1986.

Students appear to have more confidence in their mathematical abilities than affinity for the discipline . . .

CHAPTER 7
What Support and Encouragement?

School and Home Expectations

School Expectations

I N THE 1986 assessment, students were asked how much time they spent on mathematics homework each week. Most students at grades 3, 7, and 11 reported doing some mathematics homework, but from 48 to 60 percent of the students at all three grades reported spending less than an hour on this work each week.

The relationship between mathematics proficiency and reported time spent on mathematics homework for students in grades 3, 7, and 11 is presented in TABLE 7.1. Particularly at the higher grades, the more homework, the higher the mathematics proficiency. However, there were differences in this relationship across the grades. At grade 3, the highest average proficiency scores were registered by students who reported doing one-half hour of mathematics homework each week. At grades 7 and 11, students who reported investing three to four hours each week in mathematics homework exhibited the highest performance.

... the more homework, the higher the mathematics proficiency.

TABLE 7.1

Average Mathematics Proficiency by Reported Time Spent on Mathematics Homework, Grades 3, 7, and 11: 1986*

About how much time do you usually spend each week on mathematics homework?

Grade 3	Percent	Proficiency
None	13 (0.8)	214 (3.2)
½ hour	48 (1.0)	216 (1.2)
1 hour	21 (0.9)	208 (1.8)
More than 1 hour	14 (0.9)	209 (2.1)
No mathematics class	4 (0.5)	190 (2.6)
Grade 7		
No time	5 (0.5)	254 (3.7)
Less than 1 hour	43 (1.4)	265 (1.3)
1-2 hours	32 (1.3)	267 (1.3)
3-4 hours	12 (0.8)	276 (2.0)
More than 4 hours	8 (0.5)	270 (2.0)
Grade 11**		
No time	7 (0.7)	296 (4.1)
Less than 1 hour	33 (1.0)	302 (1.5)
1-2 hours	30 (1.1)	309 (2.2)
3-4 hours	18 (1.3)	323 (1.8)
More than 4 hours	13 (1.1)	320 (2.2)

*Jackknifed standard errors are presented in parentheses.
**Results are for only those students enrolled in a mathematics class at the time of the assessment.

Data on trends in the amount of time reportedly spent on mathematics homework are not available. Therefore, trend information on homework in general, rather than mathematics assignments in particular, is displayed in TABLE 7.2. Reports by 13- and 17-year-olds across assessments indicate a dramatic increase in the amount of homework being assigned every day, particularly between 1982 and 1986. In 1982, 73 percent of the 13-year-olds reported being assigned homework on a daily basis. This percentage increased to 96 percent in 1986. Results for 17-year-olds were similar, with 70 percent reporting assigned daily homework in 1982 compared to 94 percent in 1986.

In addition to the reported increase in general homework assignments, the 17-year-old students cited a significant increase in the amount of testing

How much time do you usually spend
on homework each day?

	1978		1982	
	Percent	Proficiency	Percent	Proficiency
Age 13:				
None assigned			27 (1.1)	262 (1.3)
Did not do it			6 (0.3)	269 (2.4)
Less than 1 hour	(not asked in 1978)		27 (0.5)	272 (1.3)
1-2 hours			29 (0.8)	273 (1.3)
More than 2 hours			11 (0.5)	270 (2.4)
Age 17:				
None assigned	32 (1.3)	289 (1.0)	30 (1.2)	286 (1.0)
Did not do it	13 (0.3)	302 (1.1)	12 (0.3)	303 (1.2)
Less than 1 hour	23 (0.4)	306 (1.0)	21 (0.4)	303 (1.1)
1-2 hours	23 (0.7)	309 (1.1)	26 (0.7)	304 (1.0)
More than 2 hours	10 (0.5)	315 (1.5)	12 (0.6)	309 (1.4)

*Jackknifed standard errors are presented in parentheses.

in their mathematics classes (TABLE 7.3). Eighty-two percent of the students in this age group reported frequent testing in mathematics classes in 1986 compared to only 64 percent in 1978.

The increases reported by students in the amount of time spent on homework and in the frequency of mathematics testing suggest that schools' and teachers' expectations of students are rising. These developments may be a response to the current flood of attention given to the weak academic performance of American youth. Innumerable reports have documented that in recent years, our students have not performed well in most subject areas, relative both to the past and to the abilities of their international peers. The positive relationship observed in the recent NAEP assessments between the amount of homework and proficiency scores, together with increased testing, provide hope that continued attention to these and other aspects of instruction foreshadow further gains in students' mathematical proficiency.

TABLE 7.2

	1986	
	Percent	**Proficiency**
	4 (0.7)	257 (2.6)
	3 (0.4)	262 (3.0)
	19 (0.9)	266 (1.6)
	64 (1.5)	271 (1.1)
	10 (0.7)	269 (2.6)
	6 (0.6)	283 (2.1)
	8 (0.5)	303 (2.8)
	19 (0.7)	303 (1.1)
	55 (1.3)	302 (1.0)
	12 (1.0)	313 (2.8)

Trends in Percentage of 17-Year-Olds Reporting Frequency of Testing: 1978-1986*

TABLE 7.3

How often did you take mathematics tests in your high school mathematics courses?

	Often	**Sometimes**	**Never**
1978	64 (1.3)	33 (1.1)	3 (0.5)
1982	70 (1.4)	28 (1.5)	2 (0.4)
1986	82 (1.3)	16 (1.1)	3 (0.4)

*Jackknifed standard errors are presented in parentheses.

Home Expectations

While trends in homework and testing over time indicate that academic expectations in mathematics may be rising, efforts by schools may be ineffective without additional support from home. Together, teachers and parents can help to sharpen a student's interest in mathematics—either directly, by encouraging mathematics coursetaking and helping during times of difficulty, or more indirectly, by offering positive role models and providing educational resources.

Although data on parental encouragement of students' mathematics coursetaking were not collected in previous assessments, results from 1986 are worth noting. As illustrated in TABLE 7.4, students who received at least some encouragement from their parents to take mathematics courses display

| Average Mathematics Proficiency by Level of Parental Encouragement for Mathematics Course-Taking: Grades 7 and 11: 1986* | | | | TABLE 7.4 |

	Level of Parental Encouragement		
	Great	Some	None
Grade 7	268 (0.8)	269 (1.0)	261 (2.1)
Grade 11	309 (1.3)	302 (1.1)	293 (2.2)

*Jackknifed standard errors are presented in parentheses.

higher proficiency scores than those who received none. Whether students who received a great deal of encouragement were better achievers to begin with, however, is a question that cannot be answered from the data.

Also of interest in the 1986 assessment is the positive relationship that appears to exist between students' mathematical proficiency and the level of their parents' education, depicted in TABLE 7.5. Without exception, the higher the level of parents' education, the higher the student's proficiency.

While it would be negligent to draw firm conclusions based on two discrete sets of observations—first, that level of parents' education and student proficiency are positively related, and second, that the extent of parents' encouragement in mathematics coursetaking and student proficiency are positively related—it is interesting to juxtapose the two findings. Based on the observation that parents with higher levels of education also

Average Mathematics Proficiency by Level of Parents' Education: Grades 3, 7, and 11: 1986*			TABLE 7.5

Highest Level of Parents' Education	Grade 3	Grade 7	Grade 11
Some High School	195 (2.0)	249 (0.8)	285 (1.3)
Graduated High School	206 (1.2)	261 (0.6)	294 (0.7)
Some College	218 (1.9)	275 (0.7)	307 (0.8)
Graduated College	221 (0.9)	279 (0.9)	316 (0.9)

*Jackknifed standard errors are presented in parentheses.

tended to provide their children with some or great encouragement for mathematical coursetaking, a "rich get richer" phenomenon might be posited—in that parents with higher levels of education apparently urge greater proficiency and more mathematics coursetaking from their children than do parents with less education. Whatever the interpretation of these findings, the importance of parental encouragement and education to student proficiency should be recognized.

A brief cross-cultural comparison sheds some light on the relationship between parental expectations and student abilities. A recent study of the mathematics performance of elementary school students from the United States, Taiwan, and Japan found that American children lagged far behind their foreign peers, even at the early grade levels. Other studies have reported similar findings at virtually all levels of education from elementary school through college. What was most striking in the former study was the finding that despite American students' comparatively weak mathematics performance, their parents were far more likely to be highly satisfied with their children's abilities than were parents from Taiwan and Japan—whose children demonstrated much higher mathematics proficiency.[1] If parental expectations do indeed have a bearing on students' mathematical performance, NAEP proficiency data imply that American parents may have set their sights too low.

The number and kinds of reading materials in the home may be another indicator of the value placed by parents on learning and schooling. Students in the 1986 assessment were asked about the availability of newspapers, magazines, books, and encyclopedias in the home. The mathematical proficiency scores associated with having 0-2, 3, or 4 of these types of materials is

[1]Harold Stevenson, Shin-Ying Lee, and James Stigler, "Mathematics Achievement of Chinese, Japanese and American Children." *Science*, Vol. 231, February 14, 1986, pp. 693-699.

| Trends in Performance of 9-, 13-, and 17-Year-Olds Related to Educational Materials in the Home: 1978-1986 | | | | TABLE 7.6 |

	1978	1982	1986
	Proficiency	Proficiency	Proficiency
9-Year-Olds			
0-2	201 (0.8)*	203 (1.2)*	208 (1.1)
3	221 (0.7)	221 (1.1)	224 (1.0)
4	231 (0.8)	231 (1.2)	234 (1.1)
13-Year-Olds			
0-2	239 (1.2)*	250 (1.1)	255 (2.4)
3	260 (1.2)*	267 (1.2)	266 (1.3)
4	275 (0.9)	279 (0.9)	276 (1.1)
17-Year-Olds			
0-2	277 (1.3)	281 (1.2)	281 (1.6)
3	296 (1.2)	295 (1.0)	297 (1.3)
4	308 (0.9)	306 (0.8)*	309 (1.0)

*Statistically significant difference from 1986 at the .05 level.
Jackknifed standard errors are presented in parentheses.

Trends in Performance Related to Hours of Television Watched Per Day: 1978-1986*

	1978		1982	
	Percent	Proficiency	Percent	Proficiency
Age 9:				
0-2 hours		(not asked in 1978)	44	218 (1.4)
3-5 hours			29	227 (1.1)
6 or more hours			26	215 (1.2)
Age 13:				
0-2 hours		(not asked in 1978)	45	273 (1.2)
3-5 hours			39	269 (1.1)
6 or more hours			16	256 (1.7)
Age 17:				
0-2 hours	69	305 (1.0)*	64	303 (1.0)*
3-5 hours	26	296 (1.1)	30	294 (1.0)*
6 or more hours	5	279 (2.0)	6	280 (1.4)

*Statistically significant difference from 1986 at the .05 level.
Jackknifed standard errors are presented in parentheses.

shown in TABLE 7.6. Those students who reported having all four of these types of materials showed substantially greater proficiency in mathematics than students with a smaller variety of materials.

Conversely, television is generally seen as detracting from educational achievement. In both the 1982 and 1986 assessments, students at all three ages were asked to indicate the amount of television they usually watched each day. Seventeen-year-olds were also asked this question in the 1978 assessment. Student responses were related to mathematics performance, as shown in TABLE 7.7. Students at all three age groups reported watching much more television in 1986 than they did in 1982; the percentage of students viewing 3 hours or more of television per day increased by about 11 to 17 points for all three age groups. Although the NAEP data generally indicate lower mathematics proficiency for students who watch excessive amounts of television each day, the patterns of increased viewing reported by 17-year-olds in 1986 run counter to their improved trends in proficiency. This reflects the reduced impact of television viewing on proficiency across assessments for moderate viewers (0-2 hours).

Students at all three age groups reported watching much more television in 1986 than they did in 1982 . . .

TABLE 7.7

1986	
Percent	Proficiency
29	222 (1.5)
40	229 (1.1)
31	213 (1.4)
25	276 (1.8)
55	271 (1.1)
20	255 (1.2)
45	310 (1.3)
47	299 (1.0)
9	282 (2.4)

Summary

Recent trends in the mathematics assessments indicate increased expectations on the part of schools, where both the amount of homework assigned and the frequency of testing have risen in recent years. These changes correspond to recent improvements in the mathematics performance of 9-, 13-, and 17-year-olds.

Students whose parents had higher levels of education or who encouraged mathematics coursetaking tended to have higher levels of proficiency. The amount and variety of reading materials in the home also seemed to be related to students' mathematics performance. Students at all three age groups reported watching far more television in 1986 than they did in 1982, although the relationship between these changed viewing patterns and levels of mathematics proficiency is uncertain. Thus, home and school factors— such as providing resources, encouragement, and support for mathematics learning—appear to be positively related to performance in the subject.

CHAPTER 8
Rejected Riches?

The High-School Curriculum: Mathematics Course-Taking and Program of Study

REFORMS IN mathematics classrooms—such as advancing more effective teaching methods, incorporating the benefits of calculators and computers, and raising expectation levels—mean little if high-school mathematics classes are empty. The NAEP data showed that one-quarter of the eleventh graders were not taking a mathematics class in 1986. Of those who did report being in a class, one-quarter were taking lower-level courses, such as General Mathematics, Pre-algebra, or Algebra I.

According to the Second International Mathematics Study (SIMS), a relatively large proportion of young Americans remain in school compared to young people in other countries.[1] Although the tendency is to generalize such findings about enrollment to all curriculum areas, the NAEP and SIMS data indicate that the generalization does not hold for study in mathematics. In reality, the SIMS study found that the percentage of U.S. students enrolled in advanced mathematics courses was only about average. Because a large proportion of U.S. high-school students elect to avoid mathematics courses, our nation is far from the international forefront in enrollment.

Because a large proportion of U.S. high-school students elect to avoid mathematics courses, our nation is far from the international forefront in enrollment.

[1]Curtis McKnight, et. al., *The Underachieving Curriculum: Assessing U.S. School Mathematics from an International Perspective*. A National Report on the Second International Mathematics Study, International Association for the Evaluation of Education Achievement, Stipes Publishing Company, Champaign, IL, 1987.

Part of the attrition in high-school course-taking may stem from tracking practices initiated in junior high schools. The SIMS study also showed that in contrast to other countries (most notably, Japan), the U.S. curriculum is dramatically differentiated at the eighth-grade level. In the U.S., four vastly different programs were identified, ranging from algebra for the most able students to grade school arithmetic for the least able students. In 1986, 77 percent of the seventh graders in the NAEP sample reported that they were in a regular mathematics class, 15 percent (with higher average mathematics proficiency) reported taking Pre-algebra or Algebra, and 6 percent (with much lower average proficiency) described their mathematics class as "other." This practice of early sorting may limit students' success in high school and beyond.

The Impact of Course-Taking on Mathematics Proficiency

The well-documented correspondence between mathematics course-taking and mathematics achievement is again dominant in TABLE 8.1, which displays trends in mathematics proficiency by highest level of coursework.

The positive relationship between performance and course-taking is apparent in each of the three assessments: The more advanced the course, the higher the proficiency. However, there have been some subtle changes in these relationships across time. For example in each assessment, students who had completed Algebra I or Algebra II had approximately the same levels of proficiency, respectively. Students having completed only a General Mathematics or a Pre-algebra course had higher proficiency levels in 1986 than in previous assessments, as did those having taken Pre-calculus or Calculus. In

Trends in Mathematics Proficiency for 17-Year-Olds by Highest Level of Mathematics Course: 1978-1986			TABLE 8.1

| | Age 17 | | |
	1978	1982	1986
Pre-algebra (or General Math)	267 (0.8)*	267 (0.9)*	272 (0.8)
Algebra I	286 (0.7)	287 (1.0)	287 (1.0)
Geometry	307 (0.7)*	301 (0.9)	301 (1.3)
Algebra II	321 (0.7)	318 (0.8)	320 (1.1)
Pre-calculus or Calculus	334 (1.4)*	329 (1.7)*	343 (2.7)

*Statistically significant difference from 1986 at the .05 level.
 Jackknifed standard errors are presented in parentheses.

contrast, those students having taken Geometry had lower proficiency levels in the two most recent assessments.

Trends in Mathematics Course-Taking

Patterns of course-taking also have shifted slightly across time. As shown in TABLE 8.2, the results for 17-year-olds indicate a slight decline in advanced course-taking between 1978 and 1982, with a recovery to original levels in 1986. In fact, it appears that slightly more students than in previous assessments reported taking Algebra II and Pre-calculus or Calculus. Considering the pattern of increased college entrance and graduation requirements for mathematics courses in a number of states, this finding is not surprising.

Trends in Mathematics Course-Taking: 1978-1986 Percentage of 17-Year-Olds Reporting Highest Level of Mathematics Course Taken

	Pre-algebra			Algebra I			Geometry		
	1978	1982	1986	1978	1982	1986	1978	1982	1986
Nation	22	24	19	17	16	18	16	14	17
Male	23	25	19	15	16	17	15	13	15
Female	21	24	19	18	17	18	18	15	18
White	20	22	17	17	15	17	17	15	17
Black	34	34	31	19	20	18	11	10	16
Hispanic	38	37	25	19	21	24	12	12	16

Data from the National Longitudinal Study indicated that declines in high-school course-taking occurred across the decade from 1972 to 1982.[2] Similarly, the NAEP data show that for 17-year-olds, both course-taking and proficiency declined across the 1970s and early 1980s, however upturns were evident from 1982 to 1986. Thus, the trends in course-taking reported by 17-year-olds correspond to their trends in proficiency levels.

Yet, even in 1986 a majority of students reported taking no advanced mathematics courses. While nearly 40 percent had taken Algebra II and about 7 percent had gone on to enroll in Pre-calculus or Calculus, more than half

---

[2]Ruth Ekstrom, Margaret Goertz, and Donald Rock, *Education and American Youth: The Impact of the High School Experiece*. Falmer Press, Philadelphia, PA, 1988.

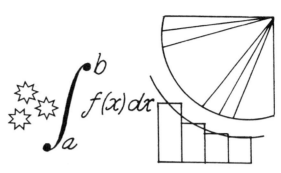

	TABLE 8.2				

Algebra II			Pre-calculus or Calculus		
1978	1982	1986	1978	1982	1986
37	39	40	6	5	7
38	39	39	7	6	8
37	39	40	4	5	5
39	41	42	6	5	7
28	29	31	4	4	3
23	24	28	3	3	6

of the 17-year-olds reported never having taken these courses. Of course, most of the 17-year-olds (90 percent) had not yet reached their senior year and would still have an opportunity to enroll in mathematics courses.

Males and females reported similar trends in course-taking across assessments, but males were slightly more likely to continue into Pre-calculus or Calculus.

The pattern for White students tended to show a dip in enrollment in 1982 for most higher level courses and then a return to 1978 levels. Hispanic students, however, showed an increase in course-taking, particularly between the last two assessments. The trends for Black students were less consistent. In 1986, more Black students reported going beyond Pre-algebra and Algebra

I to Geometry and Algebra II, yet fewer elected to enroll in Pre-calculus or Calculus than in previous years. While increases in the proportions of Black and Hispanic students taking mathematics courses are encouraging, enrollments in Algebra II are still well below those for White students.

NAEP also asked students about other mathematics courses. In each assessment, about half the 17-year-olds reported that they had taken a class in general business or consumer mathematics. In most cases, these classes were taken in addition to, rather than instead of, Pre-algebra or Algebra I. However, mathematics proficiency levels were, on average, lower for students who had taken such functionally oriented courses than they were for students who had not, indicating that the less able students—or those less mathematically inclined—may tend to fulfill their graduation requirements without taking either Geometry or Algebra II.

Average Mathematics Proficiency and Percentage of Eleventh-Grade Students in Various High School Programs by Highest Level of Mathematics Course Taken: 1986*

Program of Study	Pre-algebra	Algebra I	Geometry
Academic			
Percent	4 (0.3)	9 (0.6)	15 (0.7)
Proficiency	276 (1.5)	293 (1.1)	307 (0.8)
General			
Percent	29 (1.2)	24 (0.7)	15 (0.9)
Proficiency	270 (0.8)	286 (1.1)	299 (1.0)
Vocational/Technical			
Percent	37 (2.8)	27 (1.8)	13 (1.5)
Proficiency	271 (1.0)	286 (1.5)	298 (1.7)

*Jackknifed standard errors are presented in parentheses.

School Program and Mathematics Course-Taking

High-school students were asked whether they were enrolled in a general, academic/college preparatory, or vocational/technical school program. Nationally, 52 percent reported being in an academic or college preparatory program, 38 percent in a general program, and 10 percent in a vocational/technical program. The patterns of mathematics course selection by program placement are presented in TABLE 8.3. As anticipated, those students in academic programs are more likely to have taken advanced courses than students participating in other programs of study, and their mathematics proficiency levels reflect their course selection.

TABLE 8.3	
Algebra II	Pre-calculus or Calculus
61 (1.2)	10 (1.0)
325 (0.7)	347 (1.3)
28 (1.2)	2 (0.3)
308 (0.9)	313 (6.8)
18 (1.4)	2 (0.5)
302 (2.1)	284 (5.9)

Trends in Mathematics Proficiency by High-School Program

The two most recent assessments asked 17-year-old students about their high-school program. The average proficiency levels displayed in TABLE 8.4 show a modest, but not significant, improvement between 1982 and 1986 for students enrolled in either general or vocational/technical programs and constant levels of performance for those enrolled in academic programs.

| Trends in Average Mathematics Proficiency for 17-Year-Olds in Various High School Programs: 1982-1986* | | | | | TABLE 8.4 |

Program of Study	1982		1986	
	Percent	Proficiency	Percent	Proficiency
Academic	44	317 (0.9)	52	317 (1.0)
General	44	286 (1.0)	38	288 (1.0)
Vocational/Technical	12	283 (1.2)	10	285 (1.5)

*Jackknifed standard errors are presented in parentheses.

Summary

From an international perspective, the U.S. is only average in terms of the percentage of high-school students taking advanced mathematics courses. Although the NAEP trends indicate that after declines in the 1970s, both mathematics course enrollments and average proficiency are rising, these movements must be viewed with caution. Improvements in proficiency were centered in lower-level skills, and even in 1986, a majority of 17-year-olds reported no advanced coursework.

To retain a prominent place in today's technological world, our nation clearly needs to increase the percentage of secondary school students taking advanced mathematics classes. However, care should be taken to implement reforms at all grades, not just at the high-school level. Increasing course requirements at the upper grade levels will ensure that fewer students reject the opportunity to take more mathematics, but it will not address the fact that students in elementary and middle schools also need more challenging curricula.

Only after performance improves dramatically for younger students, particularly those in junior high school, can more high-school students take full advantage of Algebra II and Pre-calculus or Calculus courses. Throughout the school years, mathematics programs need to focus on developing the higher-level skills and concepts essential to advanced mathematics performance. Success in meeting this challenge will help to define the path of our nation's economic future.

. . . our nation clearly needs to increase the percentage of secondary school students taking advanced mathematics classes.

THE NATION'S
REPORT
CARD

naep

PROCEDURAL
APPENDIX

General Background and the Development Process

T HE NATION'S Report Card, the National Assessment of Educational Progress (NAEP), is an ongoing, congressionally mandated project established to conduct national surveys of the educational performance of young Americans. Its primary goal is to determine and report the status and trends over time in educational achievement. NAEP was created in 1969 to obtain comprehensive and dependable national educational achievement data in a uniform, scientific manner. Today, the Nation's Report Card remains the only regularly conducted national survey of educational achievement at the elementary, middle, and high-school levels.

Since 1969, NAEP has assessed 9-, 13-, and 17-year-olds attending public and private schools. In 1983, NAEP began sampling students by grade as well as by age. Because the 1985-86 assessment was the first to include grade-level samples for mathematics, the trend results presented in this report are based on comparable samples of students aged 9, 13, and 17. Some results for 1986 are also presented for students in the third, seventh, and eleventh grades.

The subject areas assessed by NAEP have included reading, writing, mathematics, science, and social studies, as well as citizenship, computer understanding, literature, art, music, and career development. Assessments

... NAEP was created in 1969 to obtain comprehensive and dependable national educational achievement data in a uniform, scientific manner.

were conducted annually through 1980 and have been conducted biennially since then. Recent assessments have included reading, writing, mathematics, science, computer understanding, literacy, literature, and U.S. history. In the 1987-88 school year, NAEP assessed reading, writing, civics, U.S. history, and geography. All subjects except career development and computer understanding have been reassessed to determine trends in achievement over time. To date, NAEP has surveyed approximately 1,300,000 American students. In addition, NAEP periodically samples young adults.

From its inception, NAEP has developed assessments through a consensus process. Educators, scholars, and citizens representative of diverse constituencies and points of view design objectives for each subject area assessment, proposing general goals they feel students should achieve in the course of their education. After careful reviews, the objectives are given to item writers, who develop assessment questions based on the objectives.

All questions
undergo exten-
sive reviews by
subject-matter
and measure-
ment specialists,
as well as care-
ful scrutiny to
eliminate any
potential bias or
lack of sensitivity
to particular
groups.

All questions undergo extensive reviews by subject-matter and measurement specialists, as well as careful scrutiny to eliminate any potential bias or lack of sensitivity to particular groups. They are then field tested, revised, and administered to a stratified, multi-stage probability sample. The young people sampled are selected so that their results may be generalized to the entire national population. Once the data have been collected, scored, and analyzed, NAEP publishes and disseminates the results. Its purpose is to provide information that will help educators, legislators, and others to improve education in the United States.

To enhance the utility of NAEP achievement results and provide the opportunity to examine policy issues, NAEP has recently begun to collect information about numerous background issues. Students, teachers, and school officials answer a variety of questions about demographics, educationally related activities and experiences, attitudes, curriculum, and resources.

NAEP is sup-
ported by the
U.S. Department
of Education,
Office of Educa-
tional Research
and Improve-
ment, Center
for Education
Statistics.

NAEP is supported by the U.S. Department of Education, Office of Educational Research and Improvement, Center for Education Statistics. In 1983, Educational Testing Service assumed the responsibility for the administration of the project, which had previously been administered by the Education Commission of the States. NAEP is governed by an independent, legislatively defined board, the Assessment Policy Committee.

General Background About NAEP's Mathematics Assessments

NAEP has assessed the mathematics achievement of in-school 9-, 13-, and 17- year-olds four times: in the 1972-73 school year, in 1977-78, in 1981-82, and in 1985-86. In 1986, NAEP also assessed the achievement of third-, seventh-, and eleventh-grade students.

For each trend assessment of the three age groups, 13-year-olds were assessed in the fall (October-December), 9-year-olds in the winter (January-February), and 17-year-olds in the spring (March-May). Birth-date ranges for each age group in each of the four trend assessments follow:

Assessment	Age 9	Age 13	Age 17
1972-73	1963	1959	10/55-9/56
1977-78	1968	1964	10/60-9/61
1981-82	1972	1968	10/64-9/65
1985-86	1976	1972	10/68-9/69

For the 1986 assessment of students at the three grade levels, all students were assessed in the spring (February-March). The target populations consisted of 9-, 13-, and 17-year-olds enrolled in public and private elementary and secondary schools, and other students in the modal grades for those ages. So that the modal grades for the three age groups would be third, seventh, and eleventh grades, the age definitions of 9- and 13-year-olds were different from those used for the trend assessments. The birthdate range for age-eligible 9-year-olds was 10/76-9/77 and for 13-year-olds was 10/72-9/73.

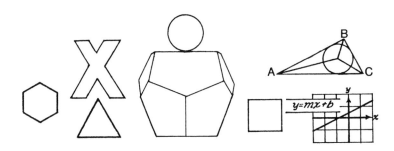

Content of the Mathematics Assessments

Each assessment contained a range of open-ended and multiple-choice questions measuring performance on sets of objectives developed by nationally representative panels of mathematics specialists, educators, and concerned citizens.[1] The objectives for each successive assessment were based on the framework used for the previous assessment, with some revisions that reflected content changes and trends in school mathematics.

---

[1] *Math Objectives, 1985-86 Assessment*. National Assessment of Educational Progress, Educational Testing Service, Princeton, NJ, 1986.

In each assessment NAEP asked students to answer questions across a range of content (e.g., numbers and operations, measurement, geometry, and algebra) and process areas (e.g., knowledge, skills, application, and problem solving). Although changes were made from assessment to assessment, a small set of exercises has been kept constant in order to anchor the results across time.

Sampling and The Trend Assessments

All NAEP assessments are based on a deeply stratified three-stage sampling design. The first stage entails defining primary sampling units (PSUs)—typically counties, but sometimes aggregates of small counties; classifying the PSUs into strata defined by region and community type; and randomly selecting PSUs. For each age level, the second stage entails enumerating, stratifying, and randomly selecting schools, both public and private, within each PSU selected at the first stage. The third stage involves randomly selecting students within a school for participation in NAEP. Some students sampled (less than 5 percent) are excluded because of limited English proficiency or severe handicap. In 1984, NAEP also began collecting descriptive information about these excluded students.

For the portion of the assessment designed to measure trends, students were administered previously assessed mathematics questions according to the procedures used in prior assessments. A total pool of 68 questions was given at age 9, 98 at age 13, and 94 at age 17, with each of the booklets accompanied by a paced audio recording of the questions as was done in the first three assessments. Because the 1986 design involved measuring trends in different subject areas at different age levels, 9- and 13-year-olds were administered any of three booklets containing mathematics trend items and 17-year-olds were administered any of two booklets.

Sample sizes for the trend results in this report and cooperation rates for the 1973, 1978, 1982, and 1986 assessments are presented below (TABLES A.1 and A.2.).

Student Sample Sizes for Mathematics Trend Scaling			TABLE A.1
	1978	**1982**	**1986**
Age 9	14,752	12,038	6,932
Age 13	24,209	15,758	6,200
Age 17 (in-school)	26,756	16,319	3,868

		Percent Schools Participating	Percent Student Completion
	Age		
1973*	9	93.9	90.9
	13	93.8	84.2
	17	92.4	73.5
1978*	9	91.5	87.2
	13	91.3	85.2
	17	89.5	73.2
1982*	9	88.3	90.5
	13	89.2	85.5
	17	86.5	74.2
1986**	9	88.7	92.9
	13	88.1	89.2
	17	82.7	78.9

School Cooperation and Student Response Rates   TABLE A.2

*1973, 1978, and 1982 figures obtained from corresponding *Public Use Data Tape User Guides.*
**1986 figures obtained from Westat, Inc., *National Assessment of Educational Progress—17th Year, Sampling and Weighting Procedures.*

The 1986 Assessment

The 1986 assessment design underlying the grade-level results was based on a powerful variant of matrix sampling called Balanced Incomplete Block (BIB) spiralling. As part of this design, for each subject area assessed (reading, science, and computer competence as well as mathematics) and for each grade level, the entire 1986 assessment battery was divided into blocks of approximately 15 minutes each, and each student was administered a booklet containing three blocks of content area materials as well as a six-minute block of background questions common to all students. Seven blocks of mathematics questions were assessed at grade 3, nine blocks at grade 7, and eleven blocks at grade 11.

As part of the partial BIB design, each pair of blocks within a subject area appeared in at least one assessment booklet. In addition, some blocks were paired across subject areas. At grade 3, 52 different booklets were prepared. Thirty-four of them contained one or more mathematics blocks, with each of the seven blocks appearing in six or eight booklets. Sixty-eight booklets were assessed at grade 7, 38 of which contained mathematics blocks; each mathe-

The 1986 assessment design underlying the grade-level results was based on a powerful variant of matrix sampling called Balanced Incomplete Block (BIB) spiralling.

126

matics block appeared in six to nine different booklets. Mathematics items were included in 41 of the 96 booklets administered to students at grade 11, with each block appearing seven to nine times.

The spiralling part of the method cycles the booklets for administration so that typically only a few students in any assessment session receive the same booklet. Across all the booklets, the grade level results contained in this report were based on 10,945 students at grade 3; 12,185 students at grade 7; and 11,850 students at grade 11.

Data Collection and Scoring

NAEP's 1985-86 assessment was conducted by a well-trained, professional data collection staff managed by Westat, Inc. Quality control was provided through site visits by NAEP and Westat staff members.

After trained readers scored the open-ended questions, the booklets were scanned and the information was transferred to the NAEP data base. These activities were conducted with particular care given to quality control procedures.

Analysis and IRT Scaling

After NAEP data were scored, they were weighted in accordance with the population structure and adjusted for nonresponse. Analyses included computing the percentage of students giving various responses and using Item Response Theory (IRT) technology to estimate levels of mathematics achievement for the nation and for various subpopulations.[2]

Using IRT technology, the performance of a sample of students in a learning area or subarea can be summarized on a single scale even if different students have been administered different exercises. The underlying principle is that when a number of items require similar skills, the regularities observed across patterns of responses can often be used to characterize both respondents and tasks in terms of a relatively small number of variables. When aggregated through appropriate mathematical formulas, these variables capture the dominant features of the data. Using the scale, it becomes possible to talk about distributions of proficiency in a population or subpopulation, and to estimate the relationships between proficiency and background variables.

Using IRT technology, the performance of a sample of students in a learning area or subarea can be summarized on a single scale even if different students have been administered different exercises.

[2]Although student responses to individual items are not discussed in this report, this information can be found in *Results from the Fourth Mathematics Assessment of the National Assessment of Educational Progress*, written by the NCTM interpretive team.

IRT defines the probability of answering a given item correctly as a mathematical function of proficiency level or skill and certain characteristics of the item. (Specifically, NAEP uses a three-parameter logistic model.) NAEP's statistical estimates of national and subgroup proficiency are computed as expected values of the figures that would have been obtained had individual proficiencies been observed, given the data that were in fact observed—the responses to the mathematics exercises and to background items. (For theoretical justification of the procedures employed and computational details, see *Implementing the New Design: The NAEP 1983-84 Technical Report*.)

The development of scales was carried out separately for the 1985-86 grade/age data and the trend data. The details of the scaling processes used appear below.

Scaling of the 1986 Grade/Age Mathematics Data

The analysis of the grade-level results of the 1986 mathematics assessment (BIB-spiral design) was carried out based on 303 items in five content area subscales. The overall composite was developed as a weighted average of subscale results. (Although this report is based on results for the grade level samples from the 1986 assessment, the age level samples were also scaled.) Each of the subscales was defined to correspond to a particular content area of mathematics as defined by the *Math Objectives, 1985-86 Assessment*.[3] The subscales were created to allow the detection of potential differences in performance patterns between content areas. The identification of the subscales, along with the number of items appearing in each subscale at each grade/age, is shown in TABLE A.3. (Items involving calculator usage were not included in the subscales.)

The construction of these subscales was along the same lines as the NAEP undimensional scales (such as Reading), with the major differences being that item parameters were estimated separately within each subscale and that, rather than estimating a single, univariate measure of proficiency, a multivariate vector of proficiencies, one for each subscale, was estimated for each student.

Like all IRT scales, the mathematics subscales have a linear indeterminacy which may be resolved by an arbitrary choice of the origin and unit-size in each given subscale. This was done for the reading scale in 1983-84 by standardizing the combined grade 4/age 9, grade 8/age 13, and grade

The subscales were created to allow the detection of potential differences in performance patterns between content areas.

---

[3]Three of the content areas defined by the *Math Objectives* book (Fundamental Methods of Mathematics, Discrete Mathematics, and Data Organization and Interpretation) had insufficient numbers of items to support the creation of subscales.

| Identification of Mathematics Subscales | | | | TABLE A.3 |

| | | Number of Items | | |
Subscale	Total	Grade 3/ Age 9	Grade 7/ Age 13	Grade 11/ Age 17
Measurement	67	26	45	39
Geometry	40	—	24	37
Relations and Functions— Algebra	38	—	—	38
Number and Operations— Higher-level Applications	78	23	50	55
Numbers and Operations— Knowledge and Skills	80	30	56	56

11/age 17 samples. Final reading results were reported on the NAEP reading proficiency scale: a 0-500 scale that represents expected number-correct scores on a hypothetical test of 500 equally spaced items.

The linear inde-
terminacies of
the mathematics
subscales were
resolved in three
steps.

The linear indeterminacies of the mathematics subscales were resolved in three steps. In the first step, intermediate transformations of each of the subscales were applied so that the age group differences across the various subscales would be approximately equal to each other. For the three subscales that spanned all three grades/ages, the intermediate transformation was accomplished by matching the mathematics age 9 and age 17 means on each subscale to the corresponding averages of the age-group means across the three subscales. Note that this method permits means to vary for the age 13 samples. For Geometry, a subscale that appeared in only the higher two age-groups, the age 17 mean was matched to the average of the age 17 means across the three-age-spanning subscales, but the age 13 mean was matched to the average transformed age 13 mean obtained in the three mathematics subscales that spanned all three ages. For the Relations and Functions— Algebra subscale, which appeared only at age 17, the mean was set to the average of the age 17 subscale means (again over the three age spanning subscales) and the standard deviation was set to the average of the age 17 standard deviations over the remaining mathematics subscales. This method of scale-determination constrains the age 9 means to be equal across subscales and the age 17 means to be equal across subscales, but the age 13 means can be expected to vary slightly.

The next step in resolving the linear indeterminacies of the subscales was the creation of an intermediate overall mathematics composite. This intermediate composite was defined separately for each grade/age as a weighted average of the estimated student proficiencies (plausible values) for the subscales appearing in that grade/age (after the intermediate transformations), with weights that reflect the number of items in that subscale on the assessment for that grade/age. (The number of items per subscale constitutes the Learning Area Committee's implicit weighting of that subscale's relative importance.) The definition of the intermediate composite in each grade/age is given in TABLE A.4.

Defining Weights for Composite Mathematics Scale*			TABLE A.4

Subscale	Grade 3/ Age 9	Grade 7/ Age 13	Grade 11/ Age 17
Measurement	28	22	17
Geometry	0	11	14
Relations and Functions— Algebra	0	0	17
Numbers and Operations— Higher-level Applications	36	33.5	26
Numbers and Operations— Knowledge and Skills	36	33.5	26
	100	100	100

*See Math Objectives, 1985-86 Assessment, p. 12.

The final step in the creation of the mathematics subscales and the composite scale was to linearly transform the intermediate composite scale so that the final composite would have a weighted mean of 250.5 and a weighted standard deviation of 50 across all students in the three grades/ages. The result is that the overall mathematics composite has the same mean and standard deviation as did the 1983-84 reading proficiency scale. The same linear transformation which created the final composite was then applied to each of the intermediate mathematics subscales.

It is necessary to caution that, although the mathematics composite is expressed in apparently the same units as the 1983-84 reading proficiency scale in that both scales have the same means and standard deviations, it is not appropriate to compare scores on one scale with scores on the other. The transformation chosen to resolve the linear indeterminacies in the mathematics composite is a convenient transformation, but is only one of a conceptually infinite number of such transformations that could have been chosen, any one of which would have provided equivalent information about the relative standings of subgroups of the population in terms of their abilities in mathematics. Because there was no link, real or implied, between mathematics and reading in the construction of the mathematics composite and the mathematics subscales, the comparison of the mean proficiencies of a subgroup on mathematics with the mean proficiencies of that subgroup on reading is not warranted and is devoid of meaning.

Scaling of the
Mathematics Trend Data

As explained previously, the measurement of trends in mathematics achievement over time was based on a somewhat different sample from that used for the 1986 grade-level results. In contrast to the BIB-spiral administration, where students read items silently to themselves in timed blocks, the method of administration in previous NAEP mathematics assessments used tape recordings to read items and pace students through the session. Furthermore, the range of birthdates that defined 9-year-old and 13-year-old students was different in the BIB-spiral administration than in previous assessments. Bridge samples of pace-administered mathematics items were included in the 1985-86 assessment in order to enable comparisons with previous NAEP assessments.[4] To adjust for the changes in age definition in the case of 9- and 13-year-old students, two separate bridge samples of pace-administered items were included in the assessment, one using the old age definitions and one the definitions used in the BIB-spiral administration. A separate IRT analysis was carried out using the bridge data from the 1985-86 assessment and data from the NAEP mathematics assessments in 1977-78 and 1981-82. The pool of items used for this scaling consisted of all items given in 1985-86 and in at least one of the previous two assessments. Due to the small number of items within subscales, a single scale was fit to these items.

These IRT analyses were carried out in the following manner: Because age samples, rather than grade/age samples, characterize the past NAEP assessments and the 1985-86 bridge sample, the three-parameter logistic IRT model was fit separately to data from each age group. A comparison of assessment results based on the bridge samples with the results from the BIB-spiral administration indicated that the trend scale could be equated to the composite mathematics scale, thereby accounting for the effects of the changes in mode of administration and definition of age. The final trend scale

---

[4] Bruce Kaplan, et al., National Assessment of Educational Progress: 1986 Bridge Studies. Final Report. Educational Testing Service, Princeton, NJ, 1988.

was determined by matching the mean and standard deviation on the IRT trend scale of the 1985-86 bridge sample (with the new age definition) to the mean and standard deviation on the composite mathematics scale of the corresponding age sample within the 1985-86 grade/age sample.

Comparison Between Mean Percent Correct and IRT Scaling

The data shown in TABLE A.5, comparing the previously reported mean percent correct for items included in the 1978 and 1982 assessments with the newly scaled mathematics analysis for these assessments, show that the trend results from 1978 to 1982 are quite similar.

Methodological Comparison of Mean Mathematics Percentage Correct* and IRT Mean Mathematics Proficiency

TABLE A.5

	Assessment Years	
	1978	1982
Age 9		
Mean Percentage Correct	55.4	56.4
Mean Proficiency	218.6	219.0
Age 13		
Mean Percentage Correct	56.7	60.5**
Mean Proficiency	264.1	268.6**
Age 17		
Mean Percentage Correct	60.3	60.2
Mean Proficiency	300.4	298.5

*From *The Third National Mathematics Assessment: Results, Trends and Issues*. National Assessment of Educational Progress, Education Commission of the States, 1983. Data are based on exercises included in both assessments.
**Statistically significant difference between 1978 and 1982 at the .05 level.

Scale Anchoring

One of NAEP's major goals has always been to describe what students know and can do and to stimulate debate about whether those levels of performance are satisfactory. An additional benefit of IRT methodology is

132

An additional benefit of IRT methodology is that it provides for a criterion-referenced interpretation of levels on a continuum of proficiency.

that it provides for a criterion-referenced interpretation of levels on a continuum of proficiency. Although the proficiency scale ranges from 0 to 500, few items fell at the ends of the continuum. Thus, levels chosen for describing results in the report are 150, 200, 250, 300, and 350. Each level is defined by describing the types of mathematics questions that most students attaining that proficiency level would be able to perform successfully; each is exemplified by typical benchmark items (see Chapter 2). Data are provided giving the estimated proportion of each age level and subgroup at or above each of the five proficiency levels.

In the scale-anchoring process, NAEP identified sets of items from the 1986 assessment that were good discriminators between proficiency levels. The guideline for selecting items was that students at any given level would have at least a 65 to 80 percent (but often higher) probability of success with these mathematics questions, while students at the next lower level would have a much lower probability of success using the criterion that the difference in probabilities exceeds 30 percent between adjacent levels. Mathematics educators examined these empirically selected item sets and used their expert judgment to characterize each proficiency level.

Extrapolating the 1973
Mean P-Value Results onto the IRT Scale

The 1973 mathematics assessment was not included in the scaling of NAEP trend data. However, for the nation and several reporting subgroups (e.g., male, female) at each of the three age levels, an estimate of the 1973 mean level of student mathematics proficiency was computed and is included in this report.

These estimates were obtained by assuming that the relationship within a given age level between the logit of a subgroup's mean p-value (i.e., mean proportion correct) and its respective mathematics proficiency mean was linear and that the same line held for all assessment years and for all subgroups within the age level. Under this assumption, the between-year difference of the mean proficiency values of a subgroup for a pair of assessment years is equal to a constant (B) times the between-year difference of the logits of the mean p-values of that subgroup for the same two years. For each age level, a mean p-value estimate using a common set of items was available for 1973, 1978, and 1982. The constant B was estimated by a regression (through the origin) of the difference between proficiency means in 1978 and 1982 on the corresponding difference between the logits of the mean p-values for these two years. All subgroups in a given age were included in the regression. The estimate of the 1973 proficiency mean for a subgroup was then obtained as the sum of the 1978 subgroup mean proficiency and B times the difference between the logits of the 1973 and 1978 subgroup mean p-values.

Estimating Variability in NAEP Measures

The standard error, computed using a jackknife replication procedure, provides an estimate of sampling reliability for NAEP measures. NAEP uses the jackknife methodology to estimate the sampling variability of all reported statistics because conventional formulas for estimating standard errors of sampling statistics are inappropriate for use with NAEP's complex sampling procedures. The standard error is composed of sampling error and other random error associated with the assessment of a specific item or set of items. Random error includes all possible nonsystematic error associated with administering specific exercise items to specific students in specific situations. The estimated population mean ± 2 standard errors represents a 95 percent confidence interval. It can be said with 95 percent certainty that the performance of the population of interest is within this interval. (For a complete description of the jackknife methodology, see *Implementing the New Design: The NAEP 1983-84 Technical Report*.) In computing significant differences across the three years, the alpha for each comparison was set at $.05/2 = .025$ to control the Type I error rate for the set of comparisons within a group.

NAEP Reporting Groups

NAEP does not report performance results for individual students, but rather for groups of students. In addition to national results, this report contains information about subgroups defined by region of the country, sex, race/ethnicity, and achievement quartiles. Definitions of these groups follow.

Region

The country has been divided into four regions: Northeast, Southeast, Central, and West. States included in each region are shown on the following map.

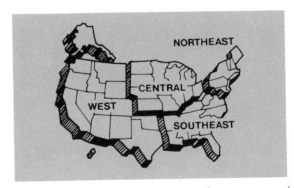

Gender

Results are reported for males and females.

Race/Ethnicity

In general, results are presented for Black, White, and Hispanic students. Following procedures used in previous assessments, trend results are based on observed racial/ethnic identifications made by assessment administrators. Grade-level results are based on student self-reports of their racial/ethnic identity according to the following categories: White, Black, Hispanic, Asian or Pacific Islander, American Indian or Alaskan Native, and Other. The sample sizes were insufficient to permit reliable estimates for the additional subgroups defined by race/ethnicity.

Quartiles

The upper quartile presents average performance for students who were in the top 25 percent on the mathematics proficiency scale; the lower quartile presents average performance for those in the bottom 25 percent.

Additional Background Factors

In addition to the standard NAEP reporting variables of region, gender, and race/ethnicity, size and type of community, and the performance quartile variable, NAEP asked all students a number of background questions. Students at grades 3 and 7 were asked about 30 questions and those at grade 11 approximately 50 questions about their school experiences and their home environment, including reading materials in the home, level of parents' education, and the time spent on homework.

Students at grades 3 and 7 were asked about 30 questions and those at grade 11 approximately 50 questions about their school experiences and their home environment . . .

In addition, background questions specific to mathematics were included in the mathematics blocks. Students at all three age/grade levels were asked questions about their coursework, their attitudes toward mathematics, and the type of instruction they had received. This describes results for some of the individual questions asked of all students, for some variables based on combining results to these questions, and for two composite variables—attitude toward mathematics and attitude toward computers.

NAEP initiated the process of developing composite variables by conducting a factor analysis of the results to the background questions specific to mathematics. Questions related to a given composite were identified and the Weighted Average Response Method (WARM) was then used to create the composite variable. An extension of the Average Response Method (ARM), the WARM technique is appropriate for constructing linear combinations of responses to background questions (i.e., factor scores) when not all sampled students have responded to all questions. (For further information about the ARM and WARM methods, see *Implementing the New Design: The NAEP 1983-84 Technical Report*).

THE NATION'S
REPORT
CARD

naep

DATA APPENDIX

Mean Mathematics Proficiency

Age 9

WEIGHTED MATHEMATICS PROFICIENCY MEANS
AND JACKNIFED STANDARD ERRORS

	1977-78	1981-82	1985-86
—TOTAL—	218.6 (0.8)*	219.0 (1.1)	221.7 (1.0)
SEX			
MALE	217.4 (0.7)*	217.1 (1.2)*	221.7 (1.1)
FEMALE	219.9 (1.0)	220.8 (1.2)	221.7 (1.2)
ETHNICITY/RACE			
WHITE	224.1 (0.9)	224.0 (1.1)	226.9 (1.1)
BLACK	192.4 (1.1)*	194.9 (1.6)*	201.6 (1.6)
HISPANIC	202.9 (2.3)	204.0 (1.3)	205.4 (2.1)
REGION			
NORTHEAST	226.9 (1.9)	225.7 (1.7)	226.0 (2.7)
SOUTHEAST	208.9 (1.2)*	210.4 (2.9)	217.8 (2.5)
CENTRAL	224.0 (1.5)	221.1 (2.4)	226.0 (2.3)
WEST	213.5 (1.4)	219.3 (1.7)	217.2 (2.4)
PARENTAL EDUCATION			
LESS THAN H.S.	200.3 (1.5)	199.0 (1.7)	200.6 (2.5)
GRADUATED H.S.	219.2 (1.1)	218.3 (1.1)	218.4 (1.6)
SOME EDUC AFTER H.S.	230.1 (1.7)	225.2 (2.1)	228.6 (2.1)
GRADUATED COLLEGE	231.3 (1.1)	228.8 (1.5)	231.3 (1.1)

Age 13

WEIGHTED MATHEMATICS PROFICIENCY MEANS
AND JACKNIFED STANDARD ERRORS

	1977-78	1981-82	1985-86
—TOTAL—	264.1 (1.1)*	268.6 (1.1)	269.0 (1.2)
SEX			
MALE	263.6 (1.3)*	269.2 (1.4)	270.0 (1.1)
FEMALE	264.7 (1.1)	268.0 (1.1)	268.0 (1.5)
ETHNICITY/RACE			
WHITE	271.6 (0.9)	274.4 (1.0)	273.6 (1.3)
BLACK	229.6 (1.9)*	240.4 (1.6)*	249.2 (2.3)
HISPANIC	238.0 (2.2)	252.4 (1.6)	254.3 (2.9)
REGION			
NORTHEAST	272.7 (2.4)	276.9 (2.2)	276.6 (2.2)
SOUTHEAST	252.7 (3.2)*	258.1 (2.4)	263.5 (1.4)
CENTRAL	269.4 (1.8)	272.8 (1.9)	266.1 (4.5)
WEST	260.0 (1.9)	266.0 (2.3)	270.4 (2.1)
PARENTAL EDUCATION			
LESS THAN H.S.	244.7 (1.2)	251.0 (1.4)	252.3 (2.3)
GRADUATED H.S.	263.1 (1.0)	262.9 (0.8)	262.7 (1.2)
SOME EDUC AFTER H.S.	273.1 (1.2)	275.1 (0.9)	273.7 (0.8)
GRADUATED COLLEGE	283.8 (1.3)	282.3 (1.5)	279.9 (1.4)

Age 17

WEIGHTED MATHEMATICS PROFICIENCY MEANS
AND JACKNIFED STANDARD ERRORS

	1977-78	1981-82	1985-86
—TOTAL—	300.4 (0.9)	298.5 (0.9)*	302.0 (0.9)
SEX			
MALE	303.8 (1.0)	301.5 (1.0)	304.7 (1.2)
FEMALE	297.1 (1.0)	295.6 (1.0)*	299.4 (1.0)
ETHNICITY/RACE			
WHITE	305.9 (0.9)	303.7 (0.9)*	307.5 (1.0)
BLACK	268.4 (1.3)*	271.8 (1.3)*	278.6 (2.1)
HISPANIC	276.3 (2.2)	276.7 (2.0)	283.1 (2.9)
REGION			
NORTHEAST	306.7 (1.7)	304.0 (2.1)	307.4 (1.9)
SOUTHEAST	292.3 (1.7)*	292.3 (2.1)	297.3 (1.4)
CENTRAL	305.2 (1.8)	302.0 (1.1)	303.6 (1.9)
WEST	295.5 (1.8)	294.1 (2.0)	299.3 (2.7)
PARENTAL EDUCATION			
LESS THAN H.S.	279.6 (1.2)	279.3 (1.0)	279.3 (2.3)
GRADUATED H.S.	293.9 (0.8)	293.4 (0.8)	293.1 (1.0)
SOME EDUC AFTER H.S.	305.3 (0.9)	303.9 (0.9)	305.2 (1.2)
GRADUATED COLLEGE	316.8 (1.0)	312.4 (1.0)	313.9 (1.4)

*SIGNIFICANT DIFFERENCE FROM 1986
AT THE .05 LEVEL.

Simple Arithmetic Facts (150)

WEIGHTED PERCENTAGE OF 9-YEAR-OLD STUDENTS WITH MATHEMATICS
PROFICIENCY AT OR ABOVE 150

	1977-78	1981-82	1985-86
—TOTAL—	96.5 (0.2)*	97.2 (0.3)	97.8 (0.2)
SEX			
MALE	95.9 (0.3)*	96.8 (0.4)	97.7 (0.3)
FEMALE	97.2 (0.3)	97.6 (0.3)	98.0 (0.3)
ETHNICITY/RACE			
WHITE	98.3 (0.2)*	98.6 (0.2)	98.9 (0.2)
BLACK	87.8 (0.9)*	90.4 (1.0)	93.0 (1.2)
HISPANIC	93.5 (1.1)	95.0 (1.0)	96.4 (1.0)
REGION			
NORTHEAST	97.8 (0.4)	98.4 (0.4)	98.6 (0.4)
SOUTHEAST	94.0 (0.6)*	94.7 (0.9)	96.9 (0.7)
CENTRAL	98.0 (0.3)*	98.0 (0.4)	98.9 (0.3)
WEST	96.1 (0.5)	97.7 (0.5)	97.0 (0.8)
PARENTAL EDUCATION			
LESS THAN H.S.	91.2 (0.8)	91.6 (1.2)	94.7 (1.7)
GRADUATED H.S.	96.9 (0.3)	97.7 (0.3)	97.7 (0.4)
SOME EDUC AFTER H.S.	98.6 (0.4)	98.6 (0.5)	98.0 (0.8)
GRADUATED COLLEGE	98.6 (0.2)	98.5 (0.3)	99.1 (0.2)

Basic Operations and Beginning Problem Solving (250)

WEIGHTED PERCENTAGE OF 9-YEAR-OLD STUDENTS WITH MATHEMATICS
PROFICIENCY AT OR ABOVE 250

	1977-78	1981-82	1985-86
—TOTAL—	19.4 (0.6)	18.7 (0.8)	20.8 (0.9)
SEX			
MALE	18.9 (0.5)	18.2 (0.9)	20.6 (0.9)
FEMALE	19.8 (0.7)	19.2 (0.9)	20.9 (1.1)
ETHNICITY/RACE			
WHITE	22.5 (0.7)	21.5 (0.9)	24.5 (1.0)
BLACK	4.3 (0.5)	4.5 (0.5)	5.4 (0.7)
HISPANIC	10.8 (1.3)	9.2 (1.1)	8.0 (2.5)
REGION			
NORTHEAST	24.9 (1.0)	23.6 (1.3)	25.0 (2.6)
SOUTHEAST	13.1 (0.7)	13.5 (1.6)	17.1 (2.2)
CENTRAL	23.0 (1.2)	19.2 (2.0)	24.8 (1.7)
WEST	15.6 (1.0)	19.0 (1.2)	16.2 (2.0)
PARENTAL EDUCATION			
LESS THAN H.S.	7.8 (0.8)	7.6 (0.7)	6.2 (2.0)
GRADUATED H.S.	19.2 (1.0)	16.2 (0.9)	17.4 (1.4)
SOME EDUC AFTER H.S.	29.0 (1.4)	24.3 (2.7)	26.4 (2.0)
GRADUATED COLLEGE	30.9 (1.1)	27.1 (1.2)	29.4 (1.2)

Beginning Skills and Understanding (200)

WEIGHTED PERCENTAGE OF 9-YEAR-OLD STUDENTS WITH MATHEMATICS
PROFICIENCY AT OR ABOVE 200

	1977-78	1981-82	1985-86
—TOTAL—	70.3 (0.9)*	71.5 (1.1)	73.9 (1.1)
SEX			
MALE	68.7 (0.9)*	68.8 (1.2)*	74.0 (1.1)
FEMALE	71.9 (1.0)	74.2 (1.2)	73.9 (1.3)
ETHNICITY/RACE			
WHITE	76.0 (0.9)	76.9 (1.1)	79.2 (1.2)
BLACK	42.5 (1.3)*	46.7 (2.3)	53.3 (2.4)
HISPANIC	54.3 (2.6)	55.0 (1.9)	58.7 (2.5)
REGION			
NORTHEAST	78.4 (2.1)	78.1 (1.9)	78.8 (2.9)
SOUTHEAST	60.7 (1.7)*	62.7 (2.6)	69.9 (2.6)
CENTRAL	75.1 (1.5)	74.1 (2.3)	76.5 (2.3)
WEST	65.9 (1.6)	71.7 (2.1)	70.9 (2.9)
PARENTAL EDUCATION			
LESS THAN H.S.	51.2 (1.9)	52.4 (1.8)	49.4 (3.4)
GRADUATED H.S.	72.1 (1.3)	72.4 (1.1)	72.5 (1.9)
SOME EDUC AFTER H.S.	79.9 (1.2)	76.6 (2.1)	79.7 (1.8)
GRADUATED COLLEGE	82.3 (1.2)	79.5 (1.4)	82.5 (1.1)

Moderately Complex Procedures and Reasoning (300)

WEIGHTED PERCENTAGE OF 9-YEAR-OLD STUDENTS WITH MATHEMATICS
PROFICIENCY AT OR ABOVE 300

	1977-78	1981-82	1985-86
—TOTAL—	0.8 (0.1)	0.6 (0.1)	0.6 (0.2)
SEX			
MALE	0.7 (0.1)	0.6 (0.1)	0.6 (0.3)
FEMALE	0.8 (0.2)	0.6 (0.1)	0.5 (0.2)
ETHNICITY/RACE			
WHITE	0.9 (0.1)	0.7 (0.1)	0.7 (0.2)
BLACK	0.0 (0.0)	0.0 (0.0)	0.0 (0.0)
HISPANIC	0.5 (0.4)	0.0 (0.0)	0.0 (0.0)
REGION			
NORTHEAST	1.1 (0.3)	1.2 (0.2)	0.8 (0.3)
SOUTHEAST	0.3 (0.1)	0.3 (0.1)	0.2 (0.1)
CENTRAL	1.3 (0.2)	0.5 (0.2)	0.9 (0.6)
WEST	0.2 (0.1)	0.5 (0.1)	0.3 (0.1)
PARENTAL EDUCATION			
LESS THAN H.S.	0.2 (0.1)	0.0 (0.0)	0.0 (0.0)
GRADUATED H.S.	0.8 (0.1)*	0.2 (0.1)	0.1 (0.1)
SOME EDUC AFTER H.S.	1.8 (0.5)	0.9 (0.4)	0.8 (0.5)
GRADUATED COLLEGE	1.3 (0.2)	1.2 (0.2)	1.1 (0.4)

(VIRTUALLY NO 9-YEAR-OLD STUDENTS HAD MATHEMATICS
PROFICIENCY AT LEVEL 350.)

*SIGNIFICANT DIFFERENCE FROM 1986
AT THE .05 LEVEL.

Percentage of Students at or Above the Five Mathematics Proficiency Levels

(VIRTUALLY ALL 13-YEAR-OLD STUDENTS HAD MATHEMATICS
PROFICIENCY AT OR ABOVE LEVEL 150.)

Beginning Skills and Understanding (200)

WEIGHTED PERCENTAGE OF 13-YEAR-OLD STUDENTS WITH MATHEMATICS
PROFICIENCY AT OR ABOVE 200

	1977-78	1981-82	1985-86
—TOTAL—	94.5 (0.4)*	97.6 (0.4)	98.5 (0.2)
SEX			
MALE	93.8 (0.5)*	97.3 (0.5)	98.3 (0.3)
FEMALE	95.1 (0.4)*	97.9 (0.2)	98.7 (0.3)
ETHNICITY/RACE			
WHITE	97.5 (0.2)*	99.1 (0.1)	99.2 (0.3)
BLACK	79.5 (1.4)*	89.0 (1.3)*	95.5 (0.8)
HISPANIC	85.9 (0.9)*	96.1 (0.8)	96.1 (1.1)
REGION			
NORTHEAST	96.1 (0.7)*	98.8 (0.3)	99.3 (0.2)
SOUTHEAST	90.3 (1.5)*	95.3 (1.0)*	98.6 (0.3)
CENTRAL	96.9 (0.4)	98.5 (0.4)	98.0 (1.0)
WEST	93.6 (0.8)*	97.5 (0.9)	98.2 (0.4)
PARENTAL EDUCATION			
LESS THAN H.S.	88.9 (0.9)*	95.2 (1.2)*	96.9 (0.8)
GRADUATED H.S.	95.9 (0.4)*	97.8 (0.4)	98.5 (0.3)
SOME EDUC AFTER H.S.	97.8 (0.4)*	98.7 (0.2)	99.5 (0.3)
GRADUATED COLLEGE	98.8 (0.2)	98.7 (0.4)	99.1 (0.2)

Basic Operations and Beginning Problem Solving (250)

WEIGHTED PERCENTAGE OF 13-YEAR-OLD STUDENTS WITH MATHEMATICS
PROFICIENCY AT OR ABOVE 250

	1977-78	1981-82	1985-86
—TOTAL—	64.9 (1.2)*	71.6 (1.2)	73.1 (1.5)
SEX			
MALE	63.7 (1.3)*	70.9 (1.4)	74.0 (1.7)
FEMALE	66.1 (1.2)*	72.3 (1.1)	72.3 (1.8)
ETHNICITY/RACE			
WHITE	72.9 (0.8)*	78.5 (0.9)	78.7 (1.6)
BLACK	28.9 (1.8)*	38.1 (1.7)*	49.4 (3.6)
HISPANIC	35.6 (2.5)*	54.2 (2.1)	55.2 (4.9)
REGION			
NORTHEAST	73.6 (2.3)	79.6 (1.6)	80.4 (2.2)
SOUTHEAST	54.2 (3.4)*	60.5 (2.1)*	68.1 (1.9)
CENTRAL	70.0 (1.8)	76.2 (2.0)	71.2 (6.1)
WEST	60.0 (2.2)*	69.2 (2.9)	73.5 (2.1)
PARENTAL EDUCATION			
LESS THAN H.S.	43.6 (1.5)*	50.1 (1.6)	56.3 (3.5)
GRADUATED H.S.	64.6 (1.1)*	67.4 (0.9)	68.9 (1.4)
SOME EDUC AFTER H.S.	75.6 (1.4)*	80.6 (1.2)	80.3 (1.6)
GRADUATED COLLEGE	84.2 (1.1)	84.5 (1.4)	83.0 (1.4)

Moderately Complex Procedures and Reasoning (300)

WEIGHTED PERCENTAGE OF 13-YEAR-OLD STUDENTS WITH MATHEMATICS
PROFICIENCY AT OR ABOVE 300

	1977-78	1981-82	1985-86
—TOTAL—	17.9 (0.7)	17.8 (0.9)	15.9 (1.0)
SEX			
MALE	18.3 (0.8)	19.2 (1.1)	17.6 (1.0)
FEMALE	17.4 (0.7)	16.3 (0.9)	14.2 (1.3)
ETHNICITY/RACE			
WHITE	21.4 (0.7)	20.9 (0.9)	18.6 (1.1)
BLACK	2.1 (0.4)	3.3 (0.9)	4.0 (1.4)
HISPANIC	3.4 (0.6)	6.2 (1.0)	5.4 (1.0)
REGION			
NORTHEAST	24.3 (1.8)	24.3 (2.3)	22.0 (2.4)
SOUTHEAST	11.6 (1.4)	10.3 (1.4)	10.8 (1.1)
CENTRAL	20.8 (1.3)*	20.3 (1.4)*	12.6 (2.4)
WEST	13.8 (1.0)	15.6 (1.6)	18.4 (2.2)
PARENTAL EDUCATION			
LESS THAN H.S.	5.8 (0.6)	5.4 (0.7)	5.3 (1.2)
GRADUATED H.S.	15.0 (0.7)*	10.6 (0.6)*	7.8 (0.8)
SOME EDUC AFTER H.S.	22.5 (0.8)*	20.5 (1.2)	17.7 (1.4)
GRADUATED COLLEGE	32.0 (1.4)*	31.3 (1.3)*	25.6 (1.3)

Multi-step Problem Solving and Algebra (350)

WEIGHTED PERCENTAGE OF 13-YEAR-OLD STUDENTS WITH MATHEMATICS
PROFICIENCY AT OR ABOVE 350

	1977-78	1981-82	1985-86
—TOTAL—	0.9 (0.2)*	0.5 (0.1)	0.4 (0.1)
SEX			
MALE	1.0 (0.2)	0.7 (0.1)	0.6 (0.2)
FEMALE	0.8 (0.2)*	0.3 (0.1)	0.2 (0.1)
ETHNICITY/RACE			
WHITE	1.1 (0.2)*	0.6 (0.1)	0.5 (0.1)
BLACK	0.0 (0.0)	0.0 (0.0)	0.1 (0.1)
HISPANIC	0.1 (0.1)	0.2 (0.1)	0.3 (0.4)
REGION			
NORTHEAST	1.4 (0.6)	1.2 (0.5)	0.7 (0.3)
SOUTHEAST	0.5 (0.1)	0.2 (0.1)	0.2 (0.1)
CENTRAL	1.1 (0.2)*	0.5 (0.1)	0.2 (0.2)
WEST	0.7 (0.2)	0.3 (0.1)	0.6 (0.3)
PARENTAL EDUCATION			
LESS THAN H.S.	0.1 (0.1)	0.0 (0.0)	0.0 (0.0)
GRADUATED H.S.	0.3 (0.1)	0.1 (0.0)	0.2 (0.1)
SOME EDUC AFTER H.S.	0.7 (0.1)	0.4 (0.1)	0.5 (0.3)
GRADUATED COLLEGE	2.7 (0.6)*	1.4 (0.4)	0.6 (0.2)

*SIGNIFICANT DIFFERENCE FROM 1986
AT THE .05 LEVEL.

(VIRTUALLY ALL 17-YEAR-OLD STUDENTS HAD MATHEMATICS PROFICIENCY AT OR ABOVE LEVEL 150.)

Beginning Skills and Understanding (200)

WEIGHTED PERCENTAGE OF 17-YEAR-OLD STUDENTS WITH MATHEMATICS PROFICIENCY AT OR ABOVE 200

	1977-78	1981-82	1985-86
—TOTAL—	99.8 (0.0)	99.9 (0.0)	99.9 (0.1)
SEX			
MALE	99.9 (0.0)	99.9 (0.0)	99.9 (0.1)
FEMALE	99.7 (0.1)	99.9 (0.0)	99.9 (0.1)
ETHNICITY/RACE			
WHITE	100.0 (0.0)	100.0 (0.0)	99.9 (0.0)
BLACK	98.7 (0.2)*	99.6 (0.2)*	100.0 (0.0)
HISPANIC	99.3 (0.2)	99.9 (0.1)	98.9 (1.1)
REGION			
NORTHEAST	99.8 (0.1)*	100.0 (0.0)	100.0 (0.0)
SOUTHEAST	99.7 (0.1)*	99.8 (0.1)	100.0 (0.0)
CENTRAL	99.9 (0.1)	100.0 (0.0)	99.9 (0.1)
WEST	99.8 (0.1)	100.0 (0.0)	99.7 (0.2)
PARENTAL EDUCATION			
LESS THAN H.S.	99.5 (0.1)*	99.9 (0.1)	100.0 (0.0)
GRADUATED H.S.	99.7 (0.1)*	99.9 (0.0)*	100.0 (0.0)
SOME EDUC AFTER H.S.	100.0 (0.0)	100.0 (0.0)	100.0 (0.0)
GRADUATED COLLEGE	100.0 (0.0)	100.0 (0.0)	100.0 (0.0)

Basic Operations and Beginning Problem Solving (250)

WEIGHTED PERCENTAGE OF 17-YEAR-OLD STUDENTS WITH MATHEMATICS PROFICIENCY AT OR ABOVE 250

	1977-78	1981-82	1985-86
—TOTAL—	92.1 (0.5)	92.9 (0.5)*	96.0 (0.4)
SEX			
MALE	93.0 (0.5)*	93.9 (0.6)*	96.5 (0.6)
FEMALE	91.2 (0.6)*	92.0 (0.5)*	95.5 (0.4)
ETHNICITY/RACE			
WHITE	95.8 (0.3)*	96.3 (0.3)*	98.3 (0.2)
BLACK	70.0 (1.4)*	75.3 (1.3)*	86.0 (1.7)
HISPANIC	77.4 (2.2)*	81.3 (1.0)*	90.8 (2.1)
REGION			
NORTHEAST	93.6 (0.6)*	95.3 (0.8)	96.4 (0.8)
SOUTHEAST	87.8 (1.3)*	88.9 (1.7)*	94.4 (1.0)
CENTRAL	94.8 (0.7)*	94.7 (0.4)*	97.5 (0.6)
WEST	90.9 (1.0)*	91.8 (0.8)*	95.4 (1.0)
PARENTAL EDUCATION			
LESS THAN H.S.	81.8 (1.0)*	84.1 (1.1)*	90.2 (1.4)
GRADUATED H.S.	90.9 (0.6)*	92.8 (0.6)	94.3 (1.0)
SOME EDUC AFTER H.S.	95.7 (0.4)*	96.1 (0.6)	97.7 (0.5)
GRADUATED COLLEGE	97.7 (0.3)	97.6 (0.3)	98.4 (0.4)

Moderately Complex Procedures and Reasoning (300)

WEIGHTED PERCENTAGE OF 17-YEAR-OLD STUDENTS WITH MATHEMATICS PROFICIENCY AT OR ABOVE 300

	1977-78	1981-82	1985-86
—TOTAL—	51.4 (1.1)	48.3 (1.2)	51.1 (1.2)
SEX			
MALE	54.9 (1.2)	51.9 (1.4)	54.2 (1.6)
FEMALE	48.0 (1.2)	44.9 (1.3)	48.1 (1.5)
ETHNICITY/RACE			
WHITE	57.3 (1.1)	54.5 (1.3)	58.0 (1.4)
BLACK	18.0 (1.3)	17.3 (1.5)	21.7 (2.6)
HISPANIC	22.1 (2.4)	20.6 (2.2)	26.8 (3.9)
REGION			
NORTHEAST	59.0 (1.9)	54.8 (2.6)	57.5 (2.6)
SOUTHEAST	42.4 (2.0)	41.3 (2.4)	45.2 (1.9)
CENTRAL	56.4 (2.1)	52.0 (1.8)	52.9 (2.5)
WEST	45.7 (2.0)	43.5 (2.7)	48.4 (3.8)
PARENTAL EDUCATION			
LESS THAN H.S.	25.8 (1.3)	23.0 (1.5)	20.0 (2.7)
GRADUATED H.S.	42.9 (1.0)	40.8 (1.1)	39.3 (1.5)
SOME EDUC AFTER H.S.	57.9 (1.1)	55.8 (1.1)	54.1 (2.1)
GRADUATED COLLEGE	71.3 (1.3)	66.9 (1.3)	68.0 (1.9)

Multi-step Problem Solving and Algebra (350)

WEIGHTED PERCENTAGE OF 17-YEAR-OLD STUDENTS WITH MATHEMATICS PROFICIENCY AT OR ABOVE 350

	1977-78	1981-82	1985-86
—TOTAL—	7.4 (0.4)	5.4 (0.4)	6.4 (0.4)
SEX			
MALE	9.5 (0.5)	6.7 (0.6)	8.2 (0.7)
FEMALE	5.5 (0.4)	4.1 (0.4)	4.5 (0.6)
ETHNICITY/RACE			
WHITE	8.6 (0.4)	6.3 (0.5)	7.6 (0.5)
BLACK	0.4 (0.2)	0.6 (0.2)	0.3 (0.2)
HISPANIC	1.1 (0.4)	0.5 (0.2)	1.2 (0.6)
REGION			
NORTHEAST	9.6 (0.9)	7.8 (1.3)	9.4 (1.6)
SOUTHEAST	5.1 (0.5)	3.8 (0.7)	4.8 (0.7)
CENTRAL	9.0 (0.7)	6.6 (0.5)	6.3 (1.0)
WEST	5.5 (0.5)	3.0 (0.2)	5.0 (1.0)
PARENTAL EDUCATION			
LESS THAN H.S.	1.3 (0.2)	0.7 (0.2)	0.4 (0.4)
GRADUATED H.S.	4.0 (0.3)	2.9 (0.3)	2.7 (0.6)
SOME EDUC AFTER H.S.	7.5 (0.5)	5.4 (0.4)	7.1 (0.8)
GRADUATED COLLEGE	14.4 (0.7)*	10.5 (1.0)	10.5 (0.9)

*SIGNIFICANT DIFFERENCE FROM 1986
AT THE .05 LEVEL.

ACKNOWLEDGMENTS

This report represents the culmination of effort by many experienced and knowledgeable people—staff and consultants who contributed their ideas, time, and energy to the development, conduct, and analysis of NAEP's mathematics assessment. Some, because of particularly significant contributions, are specifically thanked below.

Albert Beaton directs NAEP's statistical and psychometric activities. The complex mathematics analyses reported herein were designed and managed by Eugene Johnson and conducted by Edward Kulick and David Freund. Robert Mislevy designed and conducted the IRT scaling with assistance from Kathy Sheehan, Maxine Kingston, Kentaro Yamamoto, Minhwei Wang, and Jennifer Nelson. Bruce Kaplan, Ira Sample, Tom Jirele, and Tom Florek provided the graphics. John Barone directed the data analysts and provided invaluable support throughout.

The mathematics Learning Area Committee responsible for designing the assessment objectives was chaired by Iris Carl; members of the committee were James Bruni, Clyde Corcoran, Joe Crosswhite, and Shirley Hill. Item development was managed by Ann McAloon. The operational aspects of the 1985-86 assessment were managed by Nancy Mead and the complex composition and printing tasks were performed by Peter Stremic. Most of the sampling and data collection responsibility was borne by WESTAT, Inc., whose staff can only be characterized as very dedicated and extremely competent technically. Norma Norris supervised the scoring and created the data base.

The organization and writing of the report were carried out by John Dossey, Ina Mullis, Mary Lindquist, and Donald Chambers. John Dossey, past president of the National Council of Teachers of Mathematics, is a professor of Mathematics at Illinois State University. He also co-authored *The Underachieving Curriculum: Assessing U.S. School Mathematics from an International Perspective*. Ina Mullis, NAEP's Deputy Director, has been with the project since 1972 and has authored and co-authored numerous NAEP reports, including *The Reading Report Card* and *The Writing Report Card*. Mary Lindquist is chair of the NCTM task force appointed to work with ETS for the purpose of interpreting results from NAEP's fourth mathematics assessment and was a member of the NCTM task force responsible for writing portions of the NAEP report, *The Third National Mathematics Assessment: Results, Trends, and Issues*. She is the Callaway Professor of Mathematics Education at Columbus College in Columbus, Georgia. Donald Chambers is president of the Association of State Supervisors of Mathematics, and Mathematics Supervisor for the state of Wisconsin's Department of Public Instruction. He is the former president of the Wisconsin Mathematics Council, and also has extensive experience in teaching mathematics.

Special thanks for the production of this report are due to the many reviewers who suggested improvements, particularly **Anne Auman, Paul Barton, James Braswell, Joe Crosswhite, Henry Kepner, Chancey Jones, Archie Lapointe, Edward Silver** and **Beverly Whitington.** Lynn Jenkins and **Debra Kline** were instrumental in the revising and editing phase necessary to reach a final manuscript. **Kent Ashworth** and **Jan Askew** coordinated the production efforts, **Eileen Freeman** gave editorial assistance, **Bonnie Hochschild** provided composition, and **Beverly Cisney** and **Sharon Stewart** provided the excellent word-processing skills essential to the project. **Jack Weaver's** remarkable artistry and **Jan Applebaum's** graphics account for the elegance of the report.

The help of many others whose names are not identified is nonetheless gratefully acknowledged.

Since the data span a considerable period of time, it seems appropriate to recognize the pioneering and high-quality work of the Education Commission of the States, which managed the project for the first 14 years of NAEP's existence and passed on the grant to ETS in 1983 so professionally. A large portion of the data-collection responsibility prior to 1983 was borne by the Research Triangle Institute. The intelligent and consistent support of the staff and management of the U.S. Department of Education, Office of Education Research and Improvement, Center for Education Statistics is greatly appreciated.

Finally and most importantly, NAEP is grateful for the contributions of the students and school administrators who cooperated so generously.